Numerical Inversion of
the Laplace Transform

MODERN ANALYTIC AND COMPUTATIONAL METHODS IN SCIENCE AND MATHEMATICS

MÉTHODES MODERNES D'ANALYSE ET DE COMPUTATION EN SCIENCE ET MATHÉMATIQUE

NEUE ANALYTISCHE UND NUMERISCHE METHODEN IN DER WISSENSCHAFT UND DER MATHEMATIK

НОВЫЕ АНАЛИТИЧЕСКИЕ И ВЫЧИСЛИТЕЛЬНЫЕ МЕТОДЫ В НАУКЕ И МАТЕМАТИКЕ

Editorial Board

Numerical Inversion of the Laplace Transform:

Applications to Biology, Economics Engineering, and Physics

by

RICHARD BELLMAN
University of Southern California

ROBERT E. KALABA and JO ANN LOCKETT
The RAND *Corporation*

AMERICAN ELSEVIER PUBLISHING COMPANY, INC.

NEW YORK   1966

SOLE DISTRIBUTORS FOR GREAT BRITAIN

ELSEVIER PUBLISHING COMPANY, LTD.

Barking, Essex, England

SOLE DISTRIBUTORS FOR THE CONTINENT OF EUROPE

ELSEVIER PUBLISHING COMPANY

Amsterdam, The Netherlands

Library of Congress Catalog Card Number: 66-29414

CONTENTS

CHAPTER THREE

Linear Functional Equations

CHAPTER FOUR

Nonlinear Equations

CHAPTER FIVE

Dynamic Programming and Ill-Conditioned Systems

Numerical Inversion of
the Laplace Transform

INTRODUCTION

The modern approach to the study of the phenomena of the physical world, essentially the methods of Galileo, Newton, Leibniz, and their successors, relies heavily upon the use of mathematics as the language of science. The description of physical processes in this language leads to a number of functional equations, of which the most familiar are ordinary differential equations,

$$(1) \qquad \frac{dx_i}{dt} = g_i(x_1, x_2, \ldots, x_N), \qquad i = 1, 2, \ldots, N.$$

These may be subject to initial conditions such as

$$(2) \qquad x_i(0) = c_i, \qquad i = 1, 2, \ldots, N,$$

or two-point boundary-value conditions of the form

$$(3) \qquad x_i(0) = a_i, \qquad i = 1, 2, \ldots, k,$$
$$x_i(T) = b_i, \qquad i = k + 1, \ldots, N,$$

or satisfy conditions of far more complicated type involving multipoint values or integrals of the solution over the interval of interest. Almost equally familiar to the mathematical physicist and engineer are partial differential equations, such as

$$(4) \qquad u_t = u_{xx},$$

which occurs in the study of heat conduction or diffusion, or

$$(5) \qquad u_{xx} + u_{yy} = e^u,$$

which arises in magnetohydrodynamics.

These equations are deduced from certain simple assumptions made concerning the physical process under consideration. It is essential to the extension of scientific understanding that we obtain further information concerning the behavior of the physical process over time and space from an analysis of the behavior of the solution of the equation describing the process.

Thus, for example, we would like to be able to predict such qualitative properties as periodicity, boundedness, or stability directly from the structure of the equation and auxiliary conditions and to ascertain the existence and nature of steady-state behavior. In this way, we can compare predicted phenomena with observed phenomena and evaluate the significance and utility of various hypotheses and formulations. Unhappily, in many cases of importance, the complexity of the equation far exceeds the power of our mathematical capabilities. In this impasse, our only resource is a numerical solution of the equation. Indeed, only if we can derive numerical answers to numerical questions can we test plausible *a priori* assumptions and concepts against the facts of observation and experimentation. Often, only a knowledge of particular solutions tells what to look for in general and what to measure. With a sufficient number of explicit solutions in front of our eyes, we can hope to discern patterns of behavior that will aid us in our further experimentation and analysis. There is thus an intimate feedback connection between experiment and formulation on one hand and analysis and computational solution on the other.

It is because the electronic computer permits us to carry out the onerous operations required for the numerical solution of realistic descriptions of complex processes that it has assumed a paramount role in the current scientific world. Its full powers are scarcely conceived of at present; its present abilities are not used as efficiently and adroitly as they could be. It is therefore particularly important at this time of transition to spend an appreciable amount of time on the reformulation of processes and a reexamination of the methods used to study them in order to make sure that we are taking some advantage of the resources we possess.

There is much to be done before modern mathematics and modern computers become truly effective partners in scientific research.

At the present time, at one extreme we observe that far too many analytic approaches are too sophisticated for use by the mathematically nonelite. At the other extreme, we note that too many computer programs are in the nature of *tours de force* rather than routine applications of powerful methods. Much of this is a consequence of the fact that most of the mathematical formulations of physical systems in vogue today are used only because of their pedigree.

It is certainly not easy for the scientific researcher either to acquire the basic mathematical ideas or to apply complicated analytic and numerical methods. On the other hand, it is definitely inefficient and a waste of his time for him to attempt to devise his own computational algorithms—although in practice, he is often forced to do this.

We feel that the mathematician can make a significant contribution to modern scientific and technological research by providing simple, direct formulations of physical processes together with straightforward approaches to the numerical solution of the associated equations. The two aspects of problem-solving must be considered simultaneously. Our basic premise is that the availability of modern computing devices permits us in many cases to bypass the artifices, devices, and ingenuity spawned by the primitive numerical facilities of fifty, one hundred, and two hundred years ago and to provide simple, direct, easily understandable approaches.

For the reading and effective utilization of a significant quantity of the material in this book, we require only a modicum of mathematical training; say that acquired in a good course in advanced calculus. Naturally, the more mathematical training the reader has, the easier will be his task and the more he will absorb. A rudimentary knowledge of the uses of the computer will also be useful. Above all, we require a certain amount of intellectual maturity—whatever this indefinable quality is—but no more than what we know to be possessed by those currently engaged in the application of mathematical techniques to biology, economics, engineering, physics, and so on.

Our aim is to reduce the painful and time-consuming task of obtaining the numerical solution of large classes of functional equations that occur repeatedly in the description of scientific problems to a routine chore, a chore which can be delegated to assistants. In some fortunate cases, our methods can be carried out with the aid of a slide rule or a desk computer. In other cases, we may require the numerical integration of a system of ordinary differential equations or of a system of linear algebraic equations. This is the maximum of computational sophistication that we require.

The ordinary and partial differential equations of classical mathematical physics, such as those appearing in (1) and (4), arise as a consequence of plausible and convenient assumptions concerning the localization of interactions in space and time. As soon as a more realistic description of even the classical processes is attempted, we encounter more bizarre types of functional equations. Thus, for example, in chemotherapy [1,2,3],* taking account of dynamic aspects and the nonzero time required for circulation of the blood, we obtain differential-difference equations such as

(6) $$u'(t) = au(t) + bu(t - t_1),$$

and, actually, far more complicated equations, of which equations of this form are extreme simplifications. For example, in the study of respiratory models [4,5], we meet equations, such as

(7) $$u'(t) = g(u,t,u(h(u,t))),$$

in which the time lags are themselves functions of t and, indeed, of the state variables as well. Equations of this type also arise in mathematical physics.

Other processes in mathematical biology, mathematical economics, and mathematical physics give rise to equations of the form

(8) $$u(t) = f(t) + \int_0^t k(t - s)u(s)\, ds;$$

references will be found in [6,7,8]. Nonclassical approaches, such as invariant imbedding [9,10,11], and point of regeneration techniques

---

* Bracketed numbers correspond to references at the end of the chapter.

in general, applied, for example, to neutron transport processes, generate equations such as

$$(9) \qquad 2u_t + u_x = 1 + \int_0^t u_t(x,t_1)u(x,t - t_1)\,dt_1.$$

Dynamic programming applied to routing through a network leads to equations of the form

$$(10) \qquad \begin{cases} f_i(t) = \min_{j \neq i} \int_0^t f_j(s)\phi_{ij}(t - s)\,ds, & i = 1, 2, \ldots, N - 1, \\ f_N(t) = 1, \end{cases}$$

see [12,13].

It is not easy, even for the professional mathematician, to develop *ad hoc* methods for the numerical solution of functional equations of these new types. As indicated above, it is doubly difficult for the research scientist. Faced with detours of this kind, tangential to his goals, there is a natural impulse on both a conscious and subliminal level to consider simpler and less realistic, but more tractable, formulations of physical processes. This avoidance of reality is not conducive either to progress—or to the training of students.

We want to reduce the solution of transcendental functional equations of the types indicated above to the solution of much simpler and more elementary categories of equations. This is accomplished by means of a multistage process. First, we introduce an important function associated with u, the Laplace transform of the function u,

$$(11) \qquad F(s) = L(u) = \int_0^\infty u(t)e^{-st}\,dt.$$

The fundamental importance of the Laplace transform resides in its ability to lower the transcendence level of an equation. Ordinary differential equations involving $u(t)$ are reduced to algebraic equations for $F(s)$, as are also various classes of integral equations involving convolutions; partial differential equations in u are reduced to ordinary differential equations in $F(s)$.

As we shall see in the text by means of various examples, transformation of a number of strange-appearing functional equations in $u(t)$ yields tame, well-known equations for $F(s)$.

We will have succeeded in our mission of providing feasible numerical techniques if we present a simple, general technique for obtaining the values of $u(t)$, given the values of $F(s)$. An apparent flaw in this program is the well-known fact that no such technique exists! It is for this reason that many of the straightforward methods we use were resolutely ignored for quite a number of years.

What has made our efforts possible, and feasible, is the observation that we do not, in practice, want one *general* technique. Rather, we want a set of techniques, each applicable to an important subclass of problems. Here we consider one such subclass. What we demonstrate, by means of a variety of examples, is that if we restrict our attention to the class of functions $u(t)$ that arise in numerous applications, we do possess a very simple and elementary inversion method.

Specifically, we show that we can obtain excellent approximations to the values of $u(t)$ by means of a set of equations of the form

$$(12) \qquad\qquad u(t_i) = \sum_{j=1}^{N} a_{ij} F(s_j),$$

where the t_i, s_j, and a_{ij} are tabulated values.

More sophisticated techniques involving the use of quasilinearization and dynamic programming are discussed in the concluding part of the book. These are aimed at the reader with advanced training in mathematics.

Let us now briefly outline the contents of the volume. Chapter One is devoted to a presentation of the elementary properties of the Laplace transform. Chapter Two comprises a discussion of the basic concepts of numerical quadrature and the results we require for the applications in Chapter Three. As far as possible, we have tried to make the volume self-contained at the most fundamental level, in the sense of presenting all the ideas and results required for the applications. References, however, to more detailed and advanced results are given throughout. The third chapter contains sample calculations for some equations of the type described above, as well as for the heat equation

$$(13) \qquad\qquad k(x)u_t = u_{xx}.$$

In some cases, FORTRAN programs are given, together with the times required for calculation. These times, of course, depend on the computer that is used, but we feel that it is useful to give specific numbers from time to time to allow the reader to make the appropriate "change of units" from one computer to another.

Chapter Four contains a discussion of the application of successive approximations, together with the foregoing techniques, to the treatment of *nonlinear* equations. The use of the theory of quasilinearization to improve the effectiveness of successive approximations forced a consideration of linear systems of algebraic equations with nonexplicit inverses of the coefficient matrix.

This, in turn, leads us to Chapter Five, where it is shown how dynamic programming may be utilized to obtain accurate solutions of ill-conditioned systems of linear algebraic equations. This ill-conditioning, in the present instance, is a reflection of the lack of any general technique for Laplace inversion.

This work was principally motivated by aspects of our research in chemotherapy and physiological systems in general, carried out at The RAND Corporation under the support of United States Air Force Project RAND, the National Institutes of Health, and the National Aeronautics and Space Administration. A most important stimulus was also provided by our work in time-dependent transport processes, supported by the Advanced Research Projects Agency. These efforts are part of our continuing endeavor to provide the biologist, engineer, physicist, and applied mathematician with the analytic and computational tools they require to pursue their research in those areas so much wilder and untamed than the neatly mapped and well-cultivated fields of mathematics.

We have been very fortunate in obtaining careful readings of the manuscript by T. J. Higgins of the University of Wisconsin and M. Juncosa of The RAND Corporation. Both contributed a number of exceedingly helpful comments and suggestions. As always, we wish to express our appreciation of the patient and dexterous work of Jeanette Blood in typing and retyping penultimate and ultimate versions.

Following are some papers and books in the areas of mathematical biology, radiative transfer, differential-difference equations, invariant imbedding, and dynamic programming to which the reader may wish to refer for motivation, orientation, and additional references.

REFERENCES

1. R. BELLMAN, J. JACQUEZ, and R. KALABA, "Some Mathematical Aspects of Chemotherapy—I: One-organ Models," *Bull. Math. Biophys.*, Vol. 22, 1960, pp. 181–198.

2. ———, "Some Mathematical Aspects of Chemotherapy—II: The Distribution of a Drug in the Body," *Bull. Math. Biophys.*, Vol. 22, 1960, pp. 309–322.

3. ———, "Mathematical Models of Chemotherapy," *Proc. Fourth Berkeley Symposium on Mathematical Statistics and Probability*, Vol. IV, University of California Press, Berkeley, 1961, pp. 57–66.

4. J. BUELL, and F. GRODINS, *Models for the Control of Respiration*, to appear.

5. T. W. MURPHY, *A Mathematical Model of the Respiratory Controller*, to appear.

6. R. BELLMAN, and K. L. COOKE, *Differential-Difference Equations*, Academic Press, New York, 1963.

7. A. D. MYSKIS, *Linear Differential Equations with A Delayed Argument*, Moscow, 1951.

8. T. E. HARRIS, *The Theory of Branching Processes*, Springer-Verlag, Berlin, 1963.

9. R. BELLMAN, R. KALABA, and M. PRESTRUD, *Invariant Imbedding and Radiative Transfer in Slabs of Finite Thickness*, American Elsevier, New York, 1963.

10. R. BELLMAN, H. KAGIWADA, R. KALABA, and M. PRESTRUD, *Invariant Imbedding and Time-dependent Processes*, American Elsevier, New York, 1964.

11. R. BELLMAN, R. KALABA, and G. M. WING, "Invariant Imbedding and Mathematical Physics—I: Particle Processes," *J. Math. Phys.*, Vol. 1, 1960, pp. 280–308.

12. R. BELLMAN, *Dynamic Programming*, Princeton University Press, Princeton, New Jersey, 1957.
13. R. BELLMAN and S. DREYFUS, *Applied Dynamic Programming*, Princeton University Press, Princeton, New Jersey, 1962.
14. R. BELLMAN and R. KALABA, *Quasilinearization and Nonlinear Boundary-Value Problems*, American Elsevier, New York, 1965.

Chapter One

ELEMENTARY PROPERTIES OF THE LAPLACE TRANSFORM

I. INTRODUCTION

Let $u(t)$ be a function defined for $t \geq 0$. The function $F(s)$, introduced by means of the expression

$$(1.1) \qquad F(s) = \int_0^\infty e^{-st} u(t) \, dt,$$

is termed the *Laplace transform* of u. In the cases of interest in this book, the integral converges in a half plane $Re(s) > k$, and the function $F(s)$ is thereby defined in this region.

It is convenient, in order to indicate both the linear dependence on the function u and to honor Laplace, to use the notation $L(u)$. As we shall see in the pages that follow, the transform possesses a number of simple, but extremely important, properties which make it one of the most useful operations in analysis. A consequence of these properties is the remarkable way in which transformations of complicated equations for $u(t)$ result in very much simpler equations for $F(s)$.

The sections that follow lay the groundwork for the following chapters. In particular, we discuss various aspects of the task of obtaining $u(t)$, given the function $F(s)$. Throughout the book we shall dwell very fleetingly upon rigorous matters, referring the reader to a number of standard texts where detailed accounts may be found. We shall, however, endeavor as much as possible to tell the reader when and where we are taking liberties.

Fortunately, a great deal can be done with a moderate foundation in analysis.

2. CONVERGENCE

Since we shall be concerned with functions of quite simple structure in our applications of the Laplace transform in the pages that follow, the question of convergence of the integral defining $F(s)$ is completely straightforward. We suppose always that $u(t)$ satisfies a bound of the form

$$(2.1) \qquad |u(t)| \leq ae^{bt},$$

for some constants a and b, as $t \to \infty$, and that

$$(2.2) \qquad \int_0^T |u(t)|\, dt < \infty,$$

for any finite T. The combination of these two reasonable assumptions permits us to conclude that the integral converges absolutely and uniformly for $Re(s) > b$.

As a matter of fact, the key to all of our subsequent analytic and numerical work is the assumption that $u(t)$ is, for all practical purposes, well approximated by a finite sum of exponential functions,

$$(2.3) \qquad u(t) \cong \sum_{k=1}^{N} a_k e^{-kt}.$$

We discuss briefly what modifications have to be made if

$$u(t) \cong g(t)\sum_{k=1}^{N} a_k e^{-kt} \quad \text{or} \quad u(t) \cong \sum_{k=1}^{N} a_k e^{-kbt}.$$

The particular analytic form of the approximating function is not too important; what is important is that we possess a simple method for reducing the solution of an integral equation to the feasible solution of an algebraic problem, the determination of the coefficients a_k. This is the point of (2.3).

3. TRANSLATION PROPERTIES

Let us now discuss the most important of the elementary attributes of the Laplace transform, namely the relative invariance under translations in both the t- and s-spaces. We make extensive use of these properties in what follows.

The first observation is that we can write

$$(3.1) \qquad \int_0^\infty e^{-st} e^{-at} u(t)\, dt = \int_0^\infty e^{-(s+a)t} u(t)\, dt.$$

In other words,

$$(3.2) \qquad L[e^{-at} u(t)] = F(s + a).$$

Second, note that

$$(3.3) \qquad \int_1^\infty e^{-st} u(t - 1)\, dt = \int_0^\infty e^{-s(t+1)} u(t)\, dt$$

$$= e^{-s} L(u).$$

As a limiting case of this, we have

$$(3.4) \qquad L\!\left(\frac{du}{dt}\right) = \int_0^\infty e^{-st} \frac{du}{dt}\, dt$$

$$= [e^{-st} u(t)]_0^\infty + s \int_0^\infty e^{-st} u\, dt,$$

upon integrating by parts.

Supposing that

$$(3.5) \qquad \lim_{t \to \infty} e^{-st} u(t) = 0,$$

a result dictated by convergence, we obtain the basic result

$$(3.6) \qquad L\!\left(\frac{du}{dt}\right) = sL(u) - u(0).$$

Similarly,

$$(3.7) \qquad L\!\left(\frac{d^2 u}{dt^2}\right) = sL\!\left(\frac{du}{dt}\right) - u'(0)$$

$$= s^2 L(u) - su(0) - u'(0),$$

and, inductively,

$$(3.8) \qquad L\!\left(\frac{d^n u}{dt^n}\right) = s^n L(u) - s^{n-1} u(0) - \cdots - u^{(n-1)}(0).$$

Observe then the remarkable characteristic of the Laplace transform: Transformation of derivatives yields simple algebraic expressions and the operation of differentiation corresponds to the algebraic operation of multiplication. This is an example of what we mean by "reduction of transcendence."

4. THE UNRAVELING OF CONVOLUTIONS

Let us next discuss the second fundamental property of the Laplace transform. It is associated with the expression

$$(4.1) \qquad h(t) = \int_0^t f(t_1)g(t - t_1)\, dt_1.$$

This operation, creating the function $h(t)$ as a composite of the two functions $f(t)$ and $g(t)$, is one of the basic operations of analysis. It arises in analysis and mathematical physics in fundamental contexts, and in probability theory it plays an equally basic role.

The notation

$$(4.2) \qquad h = f * g$$

is frequently used to symbolize (4.1) concisely and the integral itself is termed a *convolution* in modern parlance. Observe that the ordinary integral

$$(4.3) \qquad I(f) = \int_0^t f(t_1)\, dt_1$$

is a special case of a convolution integral with $g(t) = 1$.

Let us proceed in a formal fashion to find the Laplace transform of $h(t)$. We write

$$(4.4) \qquad \int_0^\infty e^{-st} h(t)\, dt = \int_0^\infty e^{-st} \left[\int_0^t f(t_1) g(t - t_1)\, dt_1 \right] dt.$$

Consider this as a double integral over the shaded region S shown in Fig. 1.1. Ignoring any questions of the legitimacy of the interchange

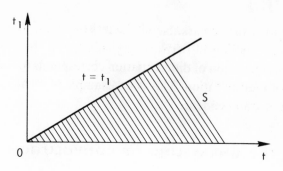

Fig. 1.1

of orders of integration, we have, upon carrying this out,

$$(4.5) \quad \iint_S e^{-st} f(t_1) g(t - t_1) \, dt \, dt_1 = \int_0^\infty f(t_1) \left[\int_{t_1}^\infty e^{-st} g(t - t_1) \, dt \right] dt_1$$

$$= \left[\int_0^\infty e^{-st_1} f(t_1) \, dt_1 \right] \left[\int_0^\infty e^{-st} g(t) \, dt \right].$$

Hence, remarkably,

$$(4.6) \qquad\qquad L(f * g) = L(f)L(g).$$

This result appears first to have been used by E. Borel.

This is another manifestation of the fact that transcendental operations in the t-plane correspond to algebraic operations in the s-plane.

5. INVERSION OF THE LAPLACE TRANSFORM

The point we are making is that $L(u)$ will, in many cases, be a much more tractable function of s than u is of t. This idea is extensively applied in what follows. Granted all of this (and many examples will certainly establish it), there nevertheless remains the basic problem: Given the values of $L(u) = F(s)$ as a function of s, how do we find the values of u as a function of t?

We can alleviate some of the suspense at the very beginning by cheerfully confessing that there is no *single* answer to this question. Instead, there are many particular methods geared to appropriate situations. This is the usual situation in mathematics and science and, hardly necessary to add, a very fortunate situation for the brotherhood. Let us now discuss some of these methods.

The simplest is that based upon the availability of a table of Laplace transforms and inverses. As might be expected, this approach is best suited for textbook exercises. Nonetheless, knowledge of exact inverses is occasionally useful for purposes of approximation.

If, as happens from time to time (see Section 2 of Chapter Three), $F(s) = L(u)$ is known as a function of a complex variable over various regions of the s-plane, we can use a complex inversion formula

$$(5.1) \qquad u(t) = \frac{1}{2\pi i} \int_C F(s)e^{st}\,ds,$$

where C is a carefully chosen contour. A particular version of (5.1) is

$$(5.2) \qquad u(t) = \lim_{T \to \infty} \frac{1}{2\pi i} \int_{b-iT}^{b+iT} F(s)e^{st}\,ds.$$

A number of analytic properties of $u(t)$ can be deduced from (5.2). Using the classical techniques of contour shifting and residue evaluation, we can obtain important information concerning the asymptotic behavior of $u(t)$ as $t \to \infty$. The drawback to this general approach is that knowledge of $F(s)$ is required in the complex plane. In many of our applications, and certainly in the most important of these, we possess information concerning $F(s)$ only on the positive part of the real axis.

There are a number of real inversion formulas, of which the best known is that of Post and Widder.* Under appropriate assumptions, one has

$$(5.3) \qquad u(t) = \lim_{k \to \infty} \left[\frac{(-1)^k}{k!}\left(\frac{k}{t}\right)^{k+1} F^{(k)}\left(\frac{k}{t}\right) \right].$$

* Here and hereafter, when the work of mathematicians is mentioned, references will be found at the end of the chapter under the corresponding section number.

Here $F^{(k)}$ denotes the k-th derivative. This can actually be used in some cases. Consider, for example, the case where

$$(5.4) \qquad e^{-\sqrt{s}} = \int_0^\infty e^{-st} \frac{e^{-\frac{1}{4}t}}{2\sqrt{\pi}\, t^{\frac{3}{2}}}\, dt.$$

Table 1.1 of values gives the approximations obtained from (5.3) for $k = 1, 2, 3$; $u_k(t)$ denotes the function inside the brackets in (5.3).

Table 1.1

t	$u_1(t)$	$u_2(t)$	$u_3(t)$	$u(t)$
0.05	0.5108	0.4191	0.3612	0.1700
0.10	0.6693	0.6989	0.7075	0.7322
0.15	0.6508	0.7347	0.7753	0.9172
0.20	0.5975	0.6964	0.7455	0.9036
0.25	0.5413	0.6429	0.6883	0.8302
0.30	0.4902	0.5829	0.6270	0.7461
0.40	0.4066	0.4834	0.5179	0.5969
0.50	0.3438	0.4060	0.4322	0.4839
0.60	0.2959	0.3463	0.3661	0.4001
0.70	0.2584	0.2996	0.3147	0.3370
0.80	0.2284	0.2624	0.2740	0.2884
0.90	0.2041	0.2323	0.2412	0.2503
1.00	0.1839	0.2075	0.2144	0.2197
1.50	0.1203	0.1307	0.1324	0.1300
2.00	0.0872	0.0920	0.0919	0.0880
2.50	0.0672	0.0693	0.0686	0.0646
3.00	0.0540	0.0546	0.0536	0.0499
3.50	0.0447	0.0445	0.0435	0.0401
4.00	0.0379	0.0372	0.0361	0.0331

It is clear that relatively small errors in the evaluation of the derivatives could seriously impair the accuracy of (5.3)—since differentiation, in general, expands inaccuracies—and thus formulas of this type will not be useful if $F(s)$ is known only through a table of values for suitable values of s. Numerical differentiation is always a risky procedure.

As stated above, and as explained below, it is *impossible* to find a completely satisfactory numerical inversion formula. This is a rather surprising state of affairs and is one of the reasons why so little practical use of the Laplace transform has been made until quite recently. As we have already indicated in the Introduction, our aim is the more modest one, to obtain an inversion technique that can be applied to a large class of problems of frequent occurrence. How we go about this is explained in Chapter Two, and what we hope is convincing proof of the feasibility of the algorithm is given in Chapters Three and Four.

Let us add that another reason for the apparent neglect of the Laplace transform is that the analytic implementation of its elegant explicit solutions often turns out to require as much, and the same kind of, effort as a direct approach.

6. INSTABILITY OF THE INVERSE OF THE LAPLACE TRANSFORM

Let $v(t)$ be a function for which

$$(6.1) \qquad \int_0^\infty |v(t)|\, e^{-kt}\, dv \le \epsilon.$$

Then, for $Re(s) \ge k$,

$$(6.2) \quad |L(u + v) - L(u)| = \left| \int_0^\infty v(t) e^{-st}\, dt \right| \le \int_0^\infty |v(t)|\, e^{-Re(s)t}\, dt \le \epsilon.$$

In other words, a "small" change in u produces an equally small change in $L(u)$. In mathematical terms, $L(u)$ is *stable* under perturbations of this type.

The impossibility of usable universal algorithms for inverting the Laplace transform is a consequence of the fact that the inverse of the Laplace transform is not stable under reasonable perturbations. Two simple examples illustrate this.

Consider first the well-known formula

$$(6.3) \qquad L(\sin at) = \frac{a}{s^2 + a^2}.$$

As a increases, the function $\sin at$ oscillates more and more rapidly, but remains of constant amplitude. The Laplace transform, however, is uniformly bounded by $1/a$ for $s \geq 0$ and thus approaches 0 uniformly as $a \to \infty$.

Consider next the formula already used,

$$(6.4) \qquad L\left(\frac{a}{2\sqrt{\pi}} \, \frac{e^{-a^2/4t}}{t^{\frac{3}{2}}} \right) = e^{-a\sqrt{s}}.$$

As $a \to 0$, the function $e^{-a\sqrt{s}}$ remains uniformly bounded by 1 for $s \geq 0$. Observe, however, how $u(t)$ behaves as a function of t. At $t = a^2/4$, we see that it has the value c_1/a^2, where c_1 is a positive constant. Nonetheless, at $t = 0$, for all $a > 0$, $u(t)$ assumes the value 0. Hence, $u(t)$ has a "spike" form (see Fig. 1.2), one which is sharper and sharper as $a \to 0$. We see then that $u(t)$ is highly localized in the vicinity of $t = 0$ for a small, and thus that $u(t)$ is an excellent approximation to the delta-function $\delta(t)$.

These examples make evident some of the difficulties we face in finding $u(t)$ given $F(s)$. Let $F(s)$ be calculated to an accuracy of 1

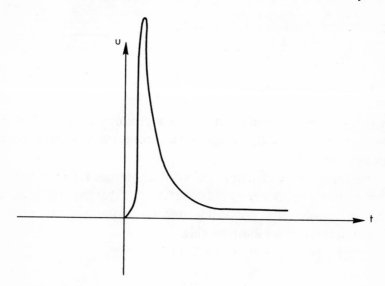

Fig. 1.2

in 10^{10}, say to ten significant figures. Then if $u_0(t)$ is the function giving rise to $F(s)$ via $F(s) = L(u_0)$, we see that

$$(6.5) \qquad u_0 + \sin 10^{20}(t - t_1) + 10^{-20} \frac{a_1 e^{-a_1^2/4(t-s_1)}}{a\sqrt{\pi}(t - s_1)^{3/2}}$$

will have, to ten significant figures, the same Laplace transform for any $a_1, s_1 > 0$.

We cannot therefore "filter out" extremely rapid oscillations or spike behavior of $u(t)$ on the basis of numerical values of $F(s)$ alone. What we can do to escape from this simultaneous nightmare and quagmire of pathological behavior is to agree to restrict our attention from the beginning to functions $u(t)$ which are essentially smooth. In other words, we can use knowledge of the structural behavior of $u(t)$ to obtain numerical values. This is the heart of our method, as indicated in Sec. 2, and it is certainly a reasonable approach. It remains to be seen whether or not it is a successful approach.

7. TAUBERIAN RESULTS

Our procedures will yield a set of values $\{u(t_i)\}$, $i = 1, 2, \ldots, N$, where $0 < t_1 < t_2 < \cdots < t_N < \infty$. If we can combine these with efficient techniques for determining the behavior of $u(t)$ as $t \to 0$ and $t \to \infty$ from the behavior of $F(s)$, then we will be able to reconstruct $u(t)$ in a quite satisfactory fashion. As we shall see subsequently, there is often need for this supplementary information since t_N may not be sufficiently large.

There is a systematic theory for obtaining information of this type. It is called *Tauberian theory* (after a German mathematician named Tauber), and was created and intensively cultivated by Hardy, Littlewood, Landau, and their students, and subsequently by Wiener.

A typical result is the following. If $u(t) \geq 0$, and

$$(7.1) \qquad F(s) = \int_0^\infty u(t)e^{-st}\, dt \sim \frac{1}{s}$$

as $s \to 0$, then

(7.2)
$$\int_0^T u(t)\, dt \sim T$$

as $T \to \infty$.*

With some further assumptions concerning $u(t)$, we can deduce the actual asymptotic behavior as $T \to \infty$.

Results of this type are easy to apply when we possess an explicit analytic representation for $L(u)$, as we do in some cases, or in various ways in a larger number of cases where we can determine the asymptotic behavior of $F(s)$ as $s \to 0$ or $s \to \infty$. Examples of this are given in Sec. 2 of Chapter Four.

The reader experienced in analysis will immediately see numerous ways of improving our techniques in particular cases. We have restrained ourselves from any display of analytic pyrotechnics in order not to obscure for the novice the simplicity of the basic approach.

BIBLIOGRAPHY AND COMMENTS

§1. Authoritative works on the Laplace transform are

D. V. WIDDER, *The Laplace Transform*, Princeton University Press, Princeton, New Jersey, 1941.

G. DOETSCH, *Handbuch der Laplace-Transformation* (3 vols.), Basel, 1950–1956.

H. BREMMER and B. VAN DER POL, *Operational Calculus Based on the Two-sided Laplace Integral*, Cambridge University Press, London, 2nd edition, 1955.

For an introductory account, together with extensive applications and references, see

R. BELLMAN and K. L. COOKE, *Differential-Difference Equations*, Academic Press, New York, 1963.

Historical remarks, further references, proofs, and detailed studies will be in each of the foregoing books.

§4. The convolution operation can be made the keystone of a theory of generalized functions, providing an alternate and simpler approach than the theory of distributions of L. Schwartz. See

A. ERDELYI, *The Operational Calculus and Generalized Functions*, Holt, Rinehart & Winston, New York, 1963.

* Here the notation $f(T) \sim g(T)$ as $T \to \infty$ signifies that $f(T)/g(T) \to 1$ as $T \to \infty$. Similarly, $F(s) \sim G(s)$ as $s \to 0$ means $F(s)/G(s) \to 1$ as $s \to 0$.

The approach along these lines is due to Mikusinski;
J. MIKUSINSKI, *Operational Calculus*, Pergamon Press, New York, 1959.
An analogue of the Laplace transform is the maximum transform,

$$F(s) = \max_{t \geq 0} [e^{-st}u(t)] = M(u).$$

It also possesses an unraveling property, namely, if

$$g(t) = \max_{t \geq t_1 \geq 0} [f(t_1)h(t - t_1)],$$

then

$$M(g) = M(f)M(h).$$

This transform is intimately connected with duality theory. For discussion and references to earlier work of Fenchel, see

R. BELLMAN, and W. KARUSH, "On a New Functional Transform in Analysis: The Maximum Transform," *Bull. Amer. Math. Soc.*, Vol. 67, 1961, pp. 501–503.

———, "Mathematical Programming and the Maximum Transform," *J. Soc. Indus. Appl. Math.*, Vol. 10, 1962, pp. 550–567.

———, "On the Maximum Transform and Semigroups of Transformations," *Bull. Amer. Math. Soc.*, Vol. 68, 1962, pp. 516–518.

———, "On the Maximum Transform," *J. Math. Anal. and Appl.*, Vol. 6, 1963, pp. 67–74.

———, "Functional Equations in the Theory of Dynamic Programming—XII: An Application of the Maximum Transform," *J. Math. Anal. and Appl.*, Vol. 6, 1963, pp. 155–157.

§5. For detailed accounts of complex inversion formulas, together with applications, see the books cited above. Thorough discussions of the Post-Widder formula will also be found there. The results in Table 1.1 were computed by O. Gross.

§6. A thorough discussion of the delta-function-like behavior of this and similar kernels will be found in Chapter 1 of

E. C. TITCHMARSH, *Introduction to the Theory of Fourier Integrals*, Oxford University Press, London, 1937.

§7. See the books by Doetsch and Widder cited above for further Tauberian theorems and applications. For an application to the determination of mean-square behavior, see

R. BELLMAN, "The Dirichlet Divisor Problem," *Duke Math. J.*, Vol. 14, 1947, pp. 411–417.

Chapter Two

NUMERICAL INVERSION OF THE LAPLACE TRANSFORM

I. INTRODUCTION

In the Introduction and in the previous chapter, we indicated some of the reasons for our interest in the Laplace transform. In this chapter we wish to describe the inversion technique we use in succeeding chapters that are devoted to applications. The basis for this technique is the method of numerical quadrature. In order to make the book as self-contained as possible, we present the rudiments of the theory of orthogonal polynomials over the interval $[-1,1]$, which is based upon the Legendre polynomials.

One of the reasons we have gone into this careful detail is that many of the fundamental properties of Legendre polynomials are valid for orthogonal polynomials with a general weighting function and are not dependent on the particular analytic structure of these functions. Consequently, the reader wishing to employ special classes of polynomials for particular processes will possess the required basic methods after going through this chapter.

The discussion is on a simple and elementary level throughout. Only at one point, in our use of Rodrigues' formula, do we invoke a *"deus ex machina."*

2. NUMERICAL QUADRATURE

The essential and completely classical idea guiding our steps in our program for the numerical inversion of the Laplace transform is that of replacing an integral by a finite sum. This quite simple and reasonable approximation procedure reduces the solution of the linear integral equation,

$$(2.1) \qquad \int_0^\infty e^{-st} u(t) \, dt = F(s),$$

to that of the solution of a system of linear algebraic equations. This by no means ends the problem, but it does serve to focus our attention and to provide a starting point for our investigation.

Let us then consider, from the beginning, the matter of obtaining an approximate expression of the type

$$(2.2) \qquad \int_a^b f(x) \, dx \cong \sum_{i=1}^N w_i f(x_i).$$

If we use digital computers, we must reduce all calculations to those of an arithmetic nature. This is the motivation for (2.2). In order to make immediate use of classical results, let us suppose that $a = -1$ and $b = 1$. If the interval (a, b) is finite, a trivial change of variable brings this about. If the interval is infinite, as it is, for example, in (2.1) a preliminary change of variable reduces it to a finite interval.

Let us note that there are many ways of reducing an infinite interval to a finite interval, each with advantages and disadvantages. We employ two, $r = e^{-t}$ and $r = t/(1 + t)$, each of which maps $0 \le t \le \infty$ in a one-to-one fashion into $0 \le r \le 1$.

We wish then to examine the approximate relation

$$(2.3) \qquad \int_{-1}^{+1} f(r) \, dr \cong \sum_{i=1}^N w_i f(r_i),$$

where the w_i and r_i are adjustable parameters. The r_i are the points at which $f(r)$ is to be evaluated and the w_i are the "weights" to be attached to these values. These weights are parameters introduced to provide additional degrees of freedom so that as few values of $f(r)$ have to be evaluated as possible. We are thinking ahead to situations where it is "expensive" for various reasons, such as time and accuracy, to have N large. Examples of this will be found in Sec. 15 of Chapter Four, and Sec. 5 of Chapter Five.

It is clearly possible to assume, without loss of generality, that the r_i are distinct and the w_i are nonzero.

Since (2.3) is an approximate relation, the first problem is that of determining how to choose the r_i and the w_i so as to obtain a reasonable approximation. For a variety of reasons which we shall not enter into here (numbering among them, however, simplicity, convenience, and custom), we shall follow a procedure inaugurated by Gauss. We require that (2.3) be *exact* for any polynomial of degree less than or equal to $2N - 1$.

It turns out, as might be expected, that this condition determines the $2N$ constants r_i and w_i, $i = 1, 2, \ldots, N$. In the following sections, we shall describe the connection between numerical quadrature and orthogonal polynomials and show how to determine the r_i and w_i in a convenient fashion.

3. THE LEGENDRE POLYNOMIALS

Let us begin, in an apparently unrelated fashion, by seeking the polynomial of degree n, $p_n(r)$, which satisfies the following $n + 1$ conditions:

(3.1) $$\int_{-1}^{1} r^m p_n(r) \, dr = 0, \qquad m = 0, 1, \ldots, n - 1,$$

$$\int_{-1}^{1} r^n p_n(r) \, dr = 1.$$

If one exists, it is unique. For, if p_n and q_n both satisfy (3.1), we have

(3.2) $$\int_{-1}^{1} r^m (p_n - q_n) \, dr = 0, \qquad m = 0, 1, 2, \ldots, n.$$

It follows that

(3.3) $$\int_{-1}^{1} g(r)(p_n - q_n) \, dr = 0$$

for any polynomial $g(r)$ of degree less than or equal to n, and thus, since $g(r) = p_n - q_n$ itself qualifies, that

(3.4) $$\int_{-1}^{1} (p_n - q_n)^2 \, dr = 0.$$

Hence, $p_n \equiv q_n$.

To establish the existence of $p_n(r)$, we could write

(3.5) $$p_n(r) = \sum_{k=0}^{n} a_k r^k,$$

and regard (3.1) as a set of $(n + 1)$ simultaneous linear algebraic equations for the coefficients a_k. Use of a famous determinantal identity of Cauchy would permit us to determine the coefficients explicitly. This is an approach we urge the reader to carry out if he has not previously come across it.

An alternate technique, ideally suited for digital computers, is the Gram-Schmidt orthogonalization procedure. Let us, however, proceed in the following different fashion which takes advantage of the simplicity of this particular case. Consider the polynomial of degree n^*,

(3.6) $$\pi_n(r) = \left(\frac{d}{dr}\right)^n (r^2 - 1)^n.$$

It is easy to see, by means of repeated integration by parts, that

(3.7) $$\int_{-1}^{+1} r^m \pi_n(r) \, dr = 0, \qquad m = 0, 1, \ldots, n - 1.$$

Furthermore, in the same fashion, we have

(3.8) $$\int_{-1}^{1} r^n \pi_n(r) \, dr = (-1)^n n! \int_{-1}^{1} (1 - r^2)^n \, dr \neq 0.$$

It is convenient to use a different normalization than that appearing in (3.1) and to introduce the functions defined by

(3.9) $$P_n(r) = \frac{1}{2^n n!} \left(\frac{d}{dr}\right)^n (r^2 - 1)^n.$$

* This is the artifice mentioned in Sec. 1.

These are the famous *Legendre polynomials* which arise in so many investigations in mathematical physics, and (3.9) is Rodrigues' formula. A steadfast integration by parts yields the result

$$(3.10) \qquad \int_{-1}^{1} P_n^2(r)\, dr = \frac{2}{2n+1}.$$

Carrying out the differentiation indicated in (3.9) gives

$$(3.11) \qquad P_n(r) = \sum_{k=0}^{m} (-1)^k \frac{(2n-2k)!\, r^{n-k}}{2^n k!(n-k)!(n-2k)!},$$

where $m = n/2$ or $(n-1)/2$, whichever is an integer. Thus,

$$(3.12) \quad P_0 = 1, \quad P_1 = r, \quad P_2 = \frac{(3r^2-1)}{2}, \quad P_3 = \frac{(5r^3-3r)}{2}.$$

4. RECURRENCE PROPERTIES OF THE LEGENDRE POLYNOMIALS

The expression in (3.11) is a dangerous formula to use routinely in connection with the numerical evaluation of $P_n(r)$ for large n because of the oscillation of the terms. We urge the reader to do some experimentation in this regard and see how quickly significant figures can be lost in evaluating the expression appearing on the right-hand side of (3.11). Only then will he appreciate why we need an alternative method for calculating the value of $P_n(r)$.

One approach is the following. In place of evaluating a polynomial $a_0 + a_1 r + \cdots + a_m r^m$ in the obvious fashion, let us write it as $(\cdots ((a_m r + a_{m-1})r + a_{m-2})r \cdots)$. This reduces the number of multiplications considerably and thus can save significant figures. Another, and perhaps more efficient, approach is based on the use of recurrence relations.

Using (3.9), it is not difficult to show that the following two recurrence relations hold:

$$(4.1) \quad (n+1)P_{n+1}(r) - (2n+1)rP_n(r) + nP_{n-1}(r) = 0, \quad n = 1, 2, \ldots,$$

$$(r^2-1)P_n'(r) = nrP_n(r) - nP_{n-1}(r), \qquad n = 1, 2, \ldots.$$

Furthermore, $P_n(r)$ satisfies the second-order linear differential equation

$$(4.2) \qquad (1 - r)^2 \frac{d^2u}{dr^2} - 2r \frac{du}{dr} + n(n + 1)u = 0.$$

The relations in (4.1) are useful in the generation of the values of $P_n(r)$ and $P_n'(r)$. Finally, let us note that (3.1) implies *orthogonality*—as also does (4.2)—i.e., that

$$(4.3) \qquad \int_{-1}^{1} P_m P_n \, dr = 0, \qquad m \neq n,$$

with

$$\int_{-1}^{1} P_n^2(r) \, dr = \frac{2}{2n + 1}.$$

This property of orthogonality is extremely important analytically and computationally. If we wish to approximate to a given function $f(r)$ over the interval $[-1,1]$ by means of a polynomial,

$$(4.4) \qquad f(r) \cong \sum_{k=0}^{N} a_k r^k,$$

it is reasonable and convenient to determine the coefficients a_k by imposing the condition that the quadratic form,

$$(4.5) \qquad \int_{-1}^{1} \left(f(r) - \sum_{k=0}^{N} a_k r^k \right)^2 dr,$$

be minimized. This leads to a system of linear algebraic equations for the a_k. Even though these can be resolved rather elegantly, the resultant expressions for the coefficients are not very useful for numerical calculation for large N, for precisely the reason discussed in connection with the formula of (3.11), namely, that we are required to solve a system of linear algebraic equations. We shall return to this point repeatedly.

If, instead of (4.4), we write

$$(4.6) \qquad f(r) \cong \sum_{k=0}^{N} b_k P_k(r),$$

an equivalent approximation, the corresponding procedure of

minimizing

$$(4.7) \qquad \int_{-1}^{1} \left(f(r) - \sum_{k=0}^{N} b_k P_k(r) \right)^2 dr$$

is readily effected.

The associated linear algebraic equations are

$$(4.8) \quad \int_{-1}^{1} \left(f(r) - \sum_{k=0}^{N} b_k P_k(r) \right) P_l(r) \, dr = 0, \qquad l = 0, 1, \ldots, N - 1.$$

By virtue of the orthogonality property, this reduces to the equation

$$(4.9) \qquad \int_{-1}^{1} f(r) P_l(r) \, dr = b_l \int_{-1}^{1} P_l^2(r) \, dr, \qquad l = 0, 1, \ldots, N - 1,$$

whence the explicit relation,

$$(4.10) \qquad b_l = \frac{(2l + 1)}{2} \int_{-1}^{1} f(r) P_l(r) \, dr.$$

5. REALITY OF ZEROES

Let us now show that the zeroes of $P_n(r)$ are real, distinct, and contained in the interval $[-1,1]$. These zeroes play an important role subsequently, which is why we dwell upon them now. The simplest proof of reality is by means of Rolle's theorem applied to Rodrigues' formula (3.9). The proof of distinctness follows from (4.1), or from the differential equation of (4.2).

Alternatively, one can use the direct definition of $P_n(r)$ in (3.1) and establish these facts along the lines of the argument used in Sec. 3 to show uniqueness. The polynomial $P_n(r)$ must change sign at least once in $[-1,1]$, as we see from the relation $\int_{-1}^{1} P_n(r) \, dr = 0$. Let $r_1, r_2, \ldots, r_m$, $1 \leq m \leq n$ be the roots of odd order in $[-1,1]$. Suppose that $m < n$. Then the expression

$$(5.1) \qquad \int_{-1}^{1} (r - r_1)(r - r_2) \cdots (r - r_m) P_n(r) \, dr$$

must be nonzero. This contradicts (3.1) for $m < n$.

6. SHIFTED LEGENDRE POLYNOMIALS

Since the quadrature formulas which we use subsequently are over the interval [0,1], let us replace the Legendre polynomials, designed for the interval [−1,1], by the *shifted Legendre polynomials*

(6.1) $$P_N^*(r) = P_N(1 - 2r).$$

The new normalization is $P_N^*(0) = 1$. Remarkably, and of course quite useful for numerical purposes, all of the coefficients in P_N^* are integers.

7. CONNECTION WITH NUMERICAL QUADRATURE

We are now ready to return to numerical quadrature. Assuming that the r_i and w_i in (2.3) are chosen according to the criterion of Gauss stated in Sec. 2, we shall show that

(7.1a) the r_i, $i = 1, 2, \ldots, N$, are the zeroes of $P_N(r)$,

(7.1b) $$w_i = \int_{-1}^{1} \frac{P_N(r)\,dr}{(r - r_i)P_N'(r_i)}, \qquad i = 1, 2, \ldots, N.$$

To establish the first part of the statement, we use the test polynomials $r^k P_N(r)$, $k = 0, 1, 2, \ldots, N - 1$, all of degree less than or equal to $2N - 1$. We obtain in this fashion the equations,

(7.2) $$0 = \int_{-1}^{1} r^k P_N(r)\, dr = \sum_{i=1}^{N} w_i r_i^k P_N(r_i),$$

$k = 0, 1, \ldots, N - 1$. Regard this as a system of N linear algebraic equations for the N quantities $w_i P_N(r_i)$, $i = 1, 2, \ldots, N$. Since the determinant,

(7.3) $|r_i^k|, \qquad i = 1, 2, \ldots, N, \qquad k = 0, 1, \ldots, N - 1,$

is a Vandermonde determinant, it follows that it is nonzero if the r_i are all distinct—as we have assumed. Hence, the only solution of (7.2) is

(7.4) $$w_i P_N(r_i) = 0, \qquad i = 1, 2, \ldots, N.$$

Since $w_i \neq 0$, we see that the r_i have the stated property.

To determine the w_i, let us use a different test polynomial, namely,

$$(7.5) \qquad f(r) = \frac{P_N(r)}{(r - r_i)P'_N(r_i)}.$$

Then

$$(7.6) \qquad f(r_j) = 0, \qquad j \neq i,$$
$$= 1, \qquad j = i.$$

Substituting in (2.3), we see that w_i is given by (7.1b).

This establishes the necessity of the conditions (7.1a) and (7.1b). Let us now demonstrate the sufficiency.

We wish to show that

$$(7.7) \qquad \int_{-1}^{1} g(r) \, dr = \sum_{i=1}^{N} w_i g(r_i)$$

if $g(r)$ is a polynomial of degree less than or equal to $2N - 1$ and the r_i and w_i are as above. Write

$$(7.8) \qquad g(r) = g_1(r)P_N(r) + g_2(r),$$

where g_1 and g_2 are both of degree at most $N - 1$.

Then we must demonstrate that

$$(7.9) \quad \int_{-1}^{1} g_1(r)P_N(r) \, dr + \int_{-1}^{1} g_2(r) \, dr = \sum_{i=1}^{N} w_i g_1(r_i)P_N(r_i) + \sum_{i=1}^{N} w_i g_2(r_i).$$

Since

$$(7.10) \qquad \int_{-1}^{1} g_1(r)P_N(r) \, dr = 0 = \sum_{i=1}^{N} w_i g_1(r_i)P_N(r_i)$$

by virtue of the properties of $P_N(r)$ and the choice of the r_i, the proof of (7.7) reduces to demonstrating that

$$(7.11) \qquad \int_{-1}^{1} g_2(r) \, dr = \sum_{i=1}^{N} w_i g_2(r_i)$$

for a polynomial of degree at most $N - 1$. Using the representation for w_i given in (7.1), it follows that

$$(7.12) \quad \sum_{i=1}^{N} w_i g_2(r_i) = \sum_{i=1}^{N} \int_{-1}^{1} \frac{P_N(r)g_2(r_i) \, dr}{(r - r_i)P'_N(r_i)} = \int_{-1}^{1} \left[\sum_{i=1}^{N} \frac{P_N(r)g_2(r_i)}{(r - r_i)P'_N(r_i)} \right] dr.$$

Consider the polynomial

(7.13) $$\sum_{i=1}^{N} \frac{P_N(r)g_2(r_i)}{(r - r_i)P'_N(r_i)}.$$

It takes the values $g_2(r_i)$ at the points $r = r_i$. As a matter of fact, we see that it is precisely the Lagrange interpolation formula for $g_2(r)$, if $g_2(r)$ is of degree $N - 1$.

The equation in (7.11) is thus established in this case. If $g_2(r)$ is of degree less than $N - 1$, we consider the new polynomial $g_2(r) + r^{N-1}$, and use the linearity of both sides of (7.7).

Finally, let us note that if we perform the change of variable

(7.14) $$\frac{1 + r}{2} = x, \qquad r = 2x - 1,$$

the previous quadrature formula becomes

(7.15) $$\int_0^1 2f(2x - 1)\, dx = \sum_{i=1}^{N} w_i f(2x_i - 1).$$

Thus, henceforth, we write

(7.16) $$\int_0^1 g(x)\, dx = \sum_{i=1}^{N} w_i g(x_i),$$

where the x_i are now the zeroes of the shifted Legendre polynomials $P_N^*(x)$ and the w_i are a new set of weights. Tables of these parameters will be found in Appendix Two.

All of our quadrature formulas are of the type given in (7.16).

Finally, let us mention a basic identity which can be used for both analytic and computational purposes. It is the Darboux-Christoffel identity which reads

(7.17) $$P_0(x)P_0(y) + P_1(x)P_1(y) + \cdots + P_N(x)P_N(y)$$
$$= \frac{k_N}{k_{N+1}} \left[\frac{P_{N+1}(x)P_N(y) - P_N(x)P_{N+1}(y)}{x - y} \right],$$

where k_N is the coefficient of x^N in $P_N(x)$. From this, we obtain both the expansion of $P_N(x)/(x - x_k)$ where x_k is a root of $P_N(x)$, but also an explicit representation for the Christoffel number appearing in (7.1b).

The result is easily established using the recurrence relation of (4.1). A detailed account of this identity will be found in the book by Szego cited at the end of the chapter.

8. NUMERICAL INVERSION OF THE LAPLACE TRANSFORM

Our aim is to determine the values of $u(t)$ as accurately as possible, given the values of $F(s)$ for $s \geq 0$ to a prescribed degree of accuracy. As above, $F(s)$ is the Laplace transform of $u(t)$,

$$(8.1) \qquad F(s) = \int_0^\infty e^{-st}u(t)\, dt.$$

The basic assumptions we make are twofold: first, that this is a well-posed problem in the sense that an exact determination of $F(s)$ would lead to an exact, and hence unique, determination of $u(t)$; second, that $u(t)$ is sufficiently "smooth" to permit the approximation methods we employ. How to recognize, *a priori*, from information concerning $F(s)$, whether these conditions are met involves a considerable amount of difficult analysis which we shall not enter into here. Our attitude will be that the "proof" is in the program—the computer program, that is. We begin with the simplest procedures and then indicate various possible modifications.

To start, a new variable of integration, $x = e^{-t}$, is introduced in order to obtain a finite interval of integration for the independent variable. Substituting, (8.1) yields

$$(8.2) \qquad \int_0^1 x^{s-1}u(-\log x)\, dx = F(s).$$

Writing $g(x) = u(-\log x)$, we may consider that we begin with the integral equation

$$(8.3) \qquad \int_0^1 x^{s-1}g(x)\, dx = F(s).$$

Applying the quadrature formula of (7.16), we obtain the approximate relation

(8.4) $$\sum_{i=1}^{N} w_i x_i^{s-1} g(x_i) = F(s).$$

Letting s assume N different values, say $s = 1, 2, \ldots, N$, yields a linear system of N equations in the N unknowns, $g(x_i)$, $i = 1, 2, \ldots, N$,

(8.5) $$\sum_{i=1}^{N} w_i x_i^k g(x_i) = F(k + 1), \qquad k = 0, 1, \ldots, N - 1,$$

and this, properly, is where our story begins.

9. INSTABILITY OF INVERSE OF THE LAPLACE TRANSFORM

As discussed in Chapter One, we cannot expect that any specific method for the inversion of the Laplace transform will work equally well in all cases. The mathematical reason for this is that the Laplace inverse is an unbounded operator. In other words, arbitrarily small changes in $F(s)$ can produce arbitrarily large changes in the value of u.

This instability manifests itself in the behavior of the matrix $\{w_i x_i^k\}$, $i = 1, 2, \ldots, N$, $k = 0, 1, \ldots, N - 1$, which is *ill-conditioned*. We shall use the term "ill-conditioned" to describe a non-singular matrix A when A^{-1} contains elements of both signs of large magnitude in such a way that a small change in the vector b produces a large change in the solution of $Ax = b$. In other words, x is an unstable function of b. The ill-conditioning of $\{w_i x_i^k\}$ rapidly worsens as N increases. The explicit inverses for various values of N given in Appendix Five illustrate this dramatically.

To appreciate what we mean by "unboundedness" or "instability," recall the following simple example discussed in Chapter One,

(9.1) $$\int_0^\infty e^{-st} \sin at \, dt = \frac{a}{s^2 + a^2}.$$

The Laplace transform is uniformly bounded by $1/a$ for $s \geq 0$.

Nevertheless, the function sin at oscillates between values of ± 1. The larger the value of a the more rapid the oscillation.

What saves the situation is the fact that in many cases, we know that the function $u(t)$ we are looking for has no high-frequency components and, as a matter of fact, is actually quite a smooth function. Consequently, we may regard the integral equation of (8.1) as defining an *equivalence class* of functions, and our objective as that of isolating the element, or set of elements, in this class with certain desired properties. What we are supposing is that $F(s)$ is determined in some fashion which inevitably associates a numerical error in the value of $F(s)$ for any particular s. This means that there are infinitely many functions $u(t)$ which satisfy the equation $L(u) \simeq F(s)$ with the prescribed degree of error. Our fundamental requirement is that $u(-\log r)$ can be well approximated by a polynomial in r for $0 \leq r \leq 1$. Our hope is that this provides the required filtering of solutions. At the moment, our concept of "well approximated" depends upon mean-square approximation. There is no reason, as indicated previously, why more sophisticated techniques should not be employed if the simple methods described herein do not suffice.

Various of the standard algorithms can be applied to the numerical solution of the linear system in (8.5). For small N, that is, $N \leq 9$, we can expect these to be reasonably successful in many problems of interest. In our early work, we employed these techniques and, fortunately, obtained satisfactory results.

Nevertheless, there are two objections to relying solely on these methods. The first is that we have no guarantee of acceptable results, since quite accurate values of $F(k)$ are often required, and the second is that the ready solution of large systems of linear algebraic equations requires a digital computer. Our aim here is to obtain a formula of the type

$$(9.2) \qquad g(x_i) = \sum_{k=0}^{N-1} a_{ik} F(k+1), \qquad i = 1, 2, \ldots, N$$

where the a_{ik} are constants independent of $F(k)$, determined once and for all for each N, and tabulated. Having accomplished this, we will have reduced the numerical inversion of the Laplace transform to an arithmetic operation that can be carried out in a few minutes at most with the aid of a desk computer and in a matter of seconds with a digital computer.

Let us therefore focus our attention on the problem of obtaining an explicit inverse for the matrix

$$(9.3) \qquad M = (w_i x_i^k).$$

In Chapter Four, in connection with *nonlinear* equations, we discuss some problems which force us to use a numerical solution of (8.5) without the aid of the explicit inverse. In Chapter Five, we employ some ideas from control theory and dynamic programming to treat these more difficult computations.

10. EXPLICIT APPROXIMATE INVERSION FORMULA

Let us make the change of variables $y_i = w_i g(x_i)$ and $a_k = F(k + 1)$, so that (8.5) takes the form

$$(10.1) \qquad \sum_{i=1}^{N} x_i^k y_i = a_k, \quad k = 0, 1, \ldots, N - 1.$$

To solve this system, we employ a classical device. Multiply the k-th equation by a parameter q_k, as yet unspecified, and add the corresponding terms in all of the equations. The result is

$$(10.2) \qquad \sum_{i=1}^{N} y_i \left(\sum_{k=0}^{N-1} q_k x_i^k \right) = \sum_{k=0}^{N-1} a_k q_k.$$

Hence, setting

$$(10.3) \qquad f(x) = \sum_{k=0}^{N-1} q_k x^k,$$

we may write

$$(10.4) \qquad \sum_{i=1}^{N} y_i f(x_i) = \sum_{k=0}^{N-1} a_k q_k,$$

where $f(x)$ is a polynominal of degree $N - 1$ to be chosen in some convenient fashion.

Our aim is to use the foregoing result valid for all such $f(x)$ to determine the y_j. To this end, suppose we demand that $f(x) = f_j(x)$ be chosen such that

(10.5) $f_j(x_i) = 0, \quad i \neq j,$

$$f_j(x_j) = 1,$$

an orthogonality condition. If $f_j(x) = \sum_{k=0}^{N-1} q_{kj} x^k$, (10.4) reduces to

(10.6) $y_j = \sum_{k=0}^{N-1} a_k q_{kj},$

where the $q_{kj}, k = 0, 1, \ldots, N - 1$, are presumably, and in actuality, determined by the conditions in (10.5).

In general, this result is interesting, but not very useful computationally. The determination of the required test polynomial $f_j(x)$, via, let us say, the Lagrange interpolation formula would in many cases introduce such numerical inaccuracy as to vitiate the entire procedure.

In our case, because of the fact that the x_i are the zeroes of the shifted Legendre polynomial P_N^*, we are most fortunate in being able to use the Lagrange interpolation formula in a meaningful fashion to obtain the explicit relation

(10.7) $f_j(x) = \dfrac{P_N^*(x)}{(x - x_j)P_N^{*\prime}(x_j)}.$

The desired q_{kj} in (10.6) are the coefficients in this polynomial of degree $N - 1$. Repeating this procedure for each j yields the desired inverse matrix, (q_{kj}).

II. NUMERICAL ASPECTS

Since the x_j are known to a high degree of accuracy and, indeed, can easily be generated to any desired degree of accuracy, and since the coefficients of the shifted Legendre polynomial, $P_N^*(x)$, are *integers*, we can by means of a tedious but conceptually simple computer program generate the values of the q_{kj}, again to any desired degree of accuracy. Having obtained the q_{kj}, we have a simple procedure for calculating the values $w_i g(x_i)$. The required values $g(x_i)$ are then obtained by division. The matrix (q_{kj}/w_k) used to convert the $F(k + 1)$ directly into the $g(x_i)$ is found in Appendix Five, for $N = 3, \ldots, 15$.

The reader may well ask at this point why it is not possible to extend the foregoing procedure in the following fashion. Using (8.4), let $s = 1, 2, \ldots, M \geq N$, and determine the values $y_i = w_i g(x_i)$, $i = 1, 2, \ldots, N$, by means of a mean-square procedure. This is to say, if y denotes the desired vector, we ask for the value of y which minimizes $(Ay - b, Ay - b)$. The required value is given as the solution of $A'Ay = A'b$.

Unfortunately, only for two values can we seem to find a simple explicit inverse of $A'A$. The first is $M = N$, and the second is $M = \infty$. This last result appears to be merely a curiosity, and one would not suspect that it would serve any useful numerical purpose.

12. INTERLACING OF THE x_{iN}

It is well known and readily proved using, say, the recurrence relations of (4.1), that between every two zeroes of $P_N^*(x)$ there is a zero of $P_{N-1}^*(x)$. In any case, we observe this from the tables of values of the roots. It follows that if we carry out the foregoing calculation for say $N = 7, 8, 9, 10$, we will obtain thirty-three different values of $g(x)$.† These values can be used as a mutual check for interpolation or extrapolation purposes and to test the accuracy of the calculation in a self-consistent fashion. We will return to this point again below.

13. CHANGE OF TIME SCALE

The procedure described for the computational inversion of the Laplace transform provides approximate values of $u(t)$ at the values

† The polynomials $P_7(r)$ and $P_9(r)$, and $P_{2N+1}(r)$ in general, share the common zero $r = 0$ ($x = \frac{1}{2}$ for $P_{2N+1}^*(x)$), which explains why $7 + 8 + 9 + 10 = 34 > 33$.

$t_i = -\log x_i$, where x_i are the N zeroes of $P_N^*(x)$. For example, when $N = 5$, these values are approximately

$$(13.1) \qquad -\log (0.0469) = 3.060,$$

$$-\log (0.231) = 1.466,$$

$$-\log (0.500) = 0.693,$$

$$-\log (0.769) = 0.262,$$

$$-\log (0.953) = 0.048.$$

Increasing N from 5 to 15 has the effect of replacing the upper bound 3.060 by 5.115 as we see from Appendix Six. This is not a significant improvement.

It is not difficult to show that the roots of $P_N^*(x)$ are uniformly distributed over $[0,1]$ to a higher and higher degree of regularity as $N \to \infty$. Unfortunately, the logarithms of the $1/x_i$ do not possess the same equidistribution property over $[0, \infty]$. Thus, the t_i values tend to bunch around $t = 0$ and to furnish meager information for large t.

Hence, we face a problem if we wish to determine $u(t)$ over a more extensive range. In some cases, as mentioned in Chapter One, we can use Tauberian methods if we are interested in the asymptotic behavior of $u(t)$; or, as also pointed out, we can occasionally use the contour integral to obtain a useful analytic expression for $u(t)$ for large t. In general, however, we must use numerical techniques. It is, however, always the case in physical processes that we possess more information concerning the solution than what occurs in a particular formulation.

Let us discuss some rudimentary techniques first. Note that if

$$(13.2) \qquad L\{u(t)\} = \int_0^\infty e^{-st}u(t)\,dt = F(s),$$

then

$$(13.3) \quad L\{u(at)\} = \int_0^\infty e^{-st}u(at)\,dt = \frac{1}{a}\int_0^\infty e^{-st/a}u(t)\,dt = \frac{F(s/a)}{a}.$$

Hence, if we use in place of $F(1)$, $F(2)$, $\ldots$, $F(N)$, the values $F(1/a)$, $F(2/a)$, $\ldots$, $F(N/a)$, we can determine, via the approximate formula

$$(13.4) \qquad \sum_{i=1}^{N} w_i x_i^{s-1} u(-a \log x_i) = \frac{F(s/a)}{a},$$

the values of $u(t)$ for the values $t = -a \log x_i$.

Observe that the coefficient matrix, and thus its inverse, are the same as before.

Alternatively, at the expense of changing the coefficient matrix, we can set $s = ka$ and consider the approximate equations

$$(13.5) \qquad \sum_{i=1}^{N} w_i x_i^{ka-1} u(-a \log x_i) = \frac{F(k)}{a}.$$

If we wish, we can determine the inverse of the matrix (x_i^{ka-1}), using a minor modification of the method given above.

In place of the polynomial $P_N^*(x)$ with the zeroes x_i, we must use the polynomial of degree N whose zeroes are x_i^k. In general, if $q(x)$ is a polynomial with the roots r_i,

$$(13.6) \qquad Q_k(x) = \prod_{j=0}^{k-1} q(x^{1/k} \omega^j),$$

where ω is a primitive k-th root of unity, is the polynomial with the zeroes r_i^k.

Thus, for example, $Q_2(x) = P_N^*(x^{\frac{1}{2}}) P_N^*(-x^{\frac{1}{2}})$ has the zeroes x_i^2, $i = 1, 2, \ldots, N$.

Having used a multiplicative property of the Laplace transform, let us now take advantage of the shifting property. Suppose that we have determined $u(t)$ at a sufficient set of points within the interval $[0, t_0]$. Then, using interpolation, we may suppose that $u(t)$ is known in this interval. Let us then write

$$(13.7) \qquad F(s) = \int_0^{\infty} e^{-st} u(t) \, dt = \int_0^{t_0} e^{-st} u(t) \, dt + \int_{t_0}^{\infty} e^{-st} u(t) \, dt$$

or

$$(13.8) \qquad F(s) - \int_0^{t_0} e^{-st} u(t) \, dt = e^{-st_0} \int_0^{\infty} e^{-st} u(t + t_0) \, dt.$$

We observe that the function $u(t + t_0)$ is the Laplace inverse of the function

$$(13.9) \qquad e^{st_0}\left[F(s) - \int_0^{t_0} e^{-st}u(t)\, dt \right].$$

Evaluating the integral

$$(13.10) \qquad \int_0^{t_0} e^{-st}u(t)\, dt$$

by means of a quadrature formula, we proceed as in the foregoing pages to obtain the values of $u(t + t_0)$ on the interval $[t_0, 2t_0]$, and so on. This method requires a high degree of accuracy on the determination of $F(s)$. In many cases, this is easy to obtain. The examples in the following chapter will illustrate this.

Using the foregoing techniques, and a method we shall discuss below in Sec. 15, we can significantly enlarge the interval of validity of the numerical inversion technique.

14. ERROR ANALYSIS

In obtaining our approximate values of $g(x)$, via (8.5), we obviously commit an error. We should solve the exact system

$$(14.1) \qquad \sum_{i=1}^{N} w_i x_i^k g(x_i) = F(k + 1) + \left(\sum_{i=1}^{N} w_i x_i^k g(x_i) - \int_0^1 x^k g(x)\, dx \right).$$

Our approximation consists of neglecting the term in parentheses.

Our tacit assumptions are:

$(14.2a)$

$$\sum_{i=1}^{N} w_i x_i^k g(x_i) - \int_0^1 x^k g(x)\, dx = \Delta_k \text{ is "small" for } k = 0, 1, 2, \ldots, N - 1,$$

and the difference between the solution of (8.5) and the solution of

$$(14.2b) \qquad \sum_{i=1}^{N} w_i x_i^k g(x_i) = F(k + 1) + \Delta_k, \quad k = 0, 1, \ldots, N - 1,$$

is "small."

Since we have the explicit inverse of the matrix $(w_i x_i^k)$, we can check the validity of (14.2b) in terms of the order of smallness of Δ_k. Such validations are usually overly pessimistic.

In practice, we obtain values of $g(x_i) = g(x_{iN})$ for different values of N, and with different degrees of accuracy in the determination of $F(k + 1)$, and compare them. If they are mutually consistent, and consistent with our analytic and physical intuition, we accept them. It is still possible, of course, to commit a systematic error in this way. Our excuse for proceeding in this fashion is twofold. First, everyone else does the same thing, and second, we do not, in general, know anything better to do.

15. EXTRAPOLATION METHODS

In many of the problems we treat in Chapter Three, we know from the analytic properties of the function $u(t)$ as a solution of the original functional equation or directly from the contour integral representation that $u(t)$ has an asymptotic expansion of the form

$$(15.1) \qquad u(t) \sim c_1 e^{\lambda_1 t} + c_2 e^{\lambda_2 t} + c_3 e^{\lambda_3 t} + \cdots,$$

as $t \to \infty$, where $0 > Re(\lambda_1) \geq Re(\lambda_2) \geq Re(\lambda_3) \geq \cdots$. In this case, in place of the usual extrapolation techniques, we can use either Rutishauser-Shanks methods, the quotient-difference algorithm, or the technique of differential approximation to obtain values of $u(t)$ for large t. At the end of the chapter references will be found to these procedures which enable us to extend the scope of the numerical inversion method presented above.

16. INVERSION OF THE MELLIN TRANSFORM

Another important functional transform in analysis and mathematical physics is the Mellin transform,

$$(16.1) \qquad M(u) = \int_0^\infty u(t)t^{s-1}\, dt,$$

usually defined for $Re(s) > 0$. Let us briefly indicate how procedures analogous to those described above can be used to obtain a numerical inversion formula.

We begin with a different change of variable

(16.2) $$t = \frac{r}{(1 - r)}, \qquad r = \frac{t}{1 + t}.$$

Then (16.1) assumes the form

(16.3) $$M(u) = F(s) = \int_0^1 \frac{u(r/(1 - r))}{(1 - r)^2}\left(\frac{r}{1 - r}\right)^{s-1} dr$$

$$= \int_0^1 g(r)\left(\frac{r}{1 - r}\right)^{s-1} dr,$$

upon simplifying the notation by setting

(16.4) $$g(r) = u(r/(1 - r))/(1 - r)^2.$$

We suppose that $u(t) \to 0$ as $t \to \infty$ rapidly enough so that $F(s)$ is defined for $Re(s) > 0$, and thus that $g(1) = 0$.

Applying an N-th order Gaussian quadrature as in the earlier sections, we have

(16.5) $$F(s) = \sum_{i=1}^{N} w_i g(r_i)\left(\frac{r_i}{1 - r_i}\right)^{s-1},$$

where the r_i are the zeroes of the shifted Legendre polynomial, $P_N^*(r)$.

Setting $s = 1, 2, \ldots, N$, we obtain N linear algebraic equations for the N quantities $w_i g(r_i)$, $i = 1, 2, \ldots, N$. Since the matrix $([r_i/(1 - r_i)]^j)$ is ill-conditioned, this is not necessarily equivalent to obtaining meaningful values for the $w_i g(r_i)$, as previously mentioned.

17. EXPLICIT MATRIX INVERSION

Let us then employ a device used in Sec. 10 to obtain an explicit analytic solution of the corresponding system obtained in connection with the Laplace transform. From (16.5), we have

(17.1) $$\sum_{k=1}^{N} a_k F_k = \sum_{i=1}^{N} w_i g(r_i)\left[\sum_{k=1}^{N-1} a_{k+1}\left(\frac{r_i}{1 - r_i}\right)^k\right]$$

for any N constants $a_1, a_2, \ldots, a_N$. We can write (17.1) in the form

$$(17.2) \qquad \sum_{k=1}^{N} a_k F_k = \sum_{i=1}^{N} w_i g(r_i) \varphi\left(\frac{r_i}{1 - r_i}\right),$$

where

$$(17.3) \qquad \varphi(x) = \sum_{k=0}^{N-1} a_{k+1} x^k,$$

a polynomial of degree $N - 1$.

Let us choose this polynomial in a convenient fashion. Suppose that

$$(17.4) \qquad \varphi\left(\frac{r_i}{1 - r_i}\right) = \delta_{ij}$$

(where δ_{ij}, the Kronecker delta function, $= 0$ if $j \neq i$, $= 1$ if $j = i$). Then if $a_{k+1,j}, k = 1, 2, \ldots, N$, are the corresponding coefficients in (17.3), we have

$$(17.5) \qquad \sum_{k=1}^{N} a_{kj} F_k = w_j g(r_j).$$

Thus, $(a_{k+1,j})$ is the required inverse matrix.

To obtain the required polynomial $\varphi_j(x)$, consider the function

$$(17.6) \qquad \pi_N(x) = P_N^*\left(\frac{x}{1 + x}\right),$$

where $P_N^*(x)$ is the shifted Legendre polynomial. We see that

$$(17.7) \qquad \pi_N\left(\frac{r_i}{1 - r_i}\right) = P_N^*(r_i) = 0, \qquad i = 1, 2, \ldots, N.$$

However, $\pi_N(x)$ is a rational function, not a polynomial. To remedy this, consider the new function,

$$(17.8) \qquad M_N(x) = (1 + x)^N \pi_N(x) = (1 + x)^N P_N^*\left(\frac{1}{1 + x}\right),$$

a polynomial of degree N. Then

$$(17.9) \qquad \varphi_j(x) = \frac{M_N(x)}{\left(x - \dfrac{r_j}{1 - r_j}\right) M_N'\left(\dfrac{r_j}{1 - r_j}\right)}$$

is the required polynomial of degree $N - 1$. Writing

$$(17.10) \qquad \varphi_j(x) = \sum_{k=0}^{N-1} a_{k+1,j} x^k,$$

we obtain the desired weighting factors. The numerical calculations required to obtain the coefficients $a_{k+1,j}$ are quite similar to those required to calculate the q_{kj} of § 10 although some additional arithmetic is needed. We have, however, not carried them out.

18. ELIMINATION OF PARTIAL DERIVATIVES

It is frequently the case that the elimination of ordinary or partial derivatives leads to a great simplification of computational effort. We have previously pointed out that the Laplace transform can be used for these purposes. Let us now indicate another technique based upon the use of the properties of the zeroes of $P_N^*(x)$, $\{x_i\}$.

Suppose that $f(x)$ is defined in $[0,1]$, and we wish to replace $f'(x_i)$ for a particular i by a linear combination of the values $f(x_j)$, $j = 1, 2, \ldots, N$,

$$(18.1) \qquad f'(x_i) \cong \sum_{j=1}^{N} a_{ij} f(x_j).$$

If we ask, in the spirit of our previous numerical quadrature, that the relation be valid for any polynomial $f(x)$ of degree less than or equal to $N - 1$, we can obtain a very simple explicit relation for the coefficients a_{ij}. Let us employ the test function

$$(18.2) \qquad f(x) = \frac{P_N^*(x)}{(x - x_k) P_N^{*\prime}(x_k)}.$$

Since $f(x_j) = 0$, $j \neq k$, $f(x_k) = 1$, we see that (18.1) becomes

$$(18.3) \qquad \left[\frac{P_N^*(x)}{(x - x_k) P_N^{*\prime}(x_k)} \right]'_{x=x} = a_{ik},$$

whence, if $k \neq i$,

$$(18.4) \qquad a_{ik} = \frac{P_N^{*\prime}(x_i)}{(x_i - x_k) P_N^{*\prime}(x_k)}.$$

If $k = i$, we use L'Hôpital's rule to obtain

(18.5) $$a_{kk} = \frac{P_N^{*''}(x_k)}{2P_N^{*'}(x_k)},$$

which, using the differential equation of (4.2), becomes

(18.6) $$a_{kk} = \frac{1 - 2x_k}{2(x_k^2 - x_k)}, \qquad k = 1, 2, \ldots, N.$$

19. INVERSION TECHNIQUES OF OTHER TYPES

At this point, the reader may well ask the reason for the artificial transformation of the interval $[0, \infty]$ into the interval $[0,1]$. Why not carry out the indicated techniques directly for the interval $[0, \infty]$? We cannot, of course, write

(19.1) $$u(t) \sim \sum_{k=0}^{N} a_k t^k$$

for $0 \leq t < \infty$, and seek to determine the a_k by means of the minimization of

(19.2) $$\int_0^\infty \left(u(t) - \sum_{k=0}^{N} a_k t^k \right)^2 dt.$$

To avoid the difficulty of the divergence of the integral, we can introduce a convergence factor such as e^{-t}, and seek to minimize the expression

(19.3) $$\int_0^\infty e^{-t} \left(u(t) - \sum_{k=0}^{N} a_k t^k \right)^2 dt.$$

With the aid of this convergence factor, and under the assumption that $u(t)$ does not increase too rapidly as $t \to \infty$, we can parallel all of the preceding development. The polynomials obtained in this way are the *Laguerre polynomials*.

There is a corresponding quadrature formula

(19.4) $$\int_0^\infty g(t)\, dt \cong \sum_{i=1}^{N} w_i g(t_i),$$

and we can use it to invert the Laplace transform in a fashion completely analogous to that given above.

If we suspect that $u(t)$ has a different asymptotic behavior as

$t \to \infty$, then we can use still other classes of orthogonal polynomials. Many different useful classes are described in the book by Szego cited at the end of the chapter.

Furthermore, we can approximate in the s-plane as well as the t-plane. If

(19.5)
$$F(s) \cong \sum_{k=1}^{N} \frac{a_k}{s + \lambda_k},$$

for $s \geq 0$, then we expect

(19.6)
$$u(t) \cong \sum_{k=1}^{N} a_k e^{-\lambda_k t}.$$

There are many ways of obtaining the a_k and λ_k. For example, we can think in terms of Padé approximations and continued fractions.

We have employed the Legendre polynomials in what follows for several reasons. First, by virtue of our work in radiative transfer, we had already established a *modus vivendi*, in the sense that the tables of values of quadrature points and weights were readily available. Second, the procedures worked quite well in the cases we tried. Third, the techniques were easily described and required little analytic background.

None of these reasons are particularly significant at the present time or in the future when the corresponding values for Laguerre and more general polynomials are equally available or are easily generated in a few seconds of computer time and when the mathematical sophistication of scientists in all areas is increasing at such a rapid rate. What method should be used?

Our feeling is that several methods should be employed concurrently, both to check the accuracy of each and to obtain a large number of values of $u(t)$. Certainly, the future of numerical analysis lies in the development of parallel and sequential techniques, a concept we shall discuss in Chapter Five. Our aim here is merely to indicate the simplicity and efficacy of the over-all concept of the use of transform techniques for computational purposes and certainly not to freeze the field of numerical inversion of the Laplace transform into some premature and definitely immature orthodoxy.

BIBLIOGRAPHY AND COMMENTS

§1. For a detailed discussion of numerical quadrature, see

C. LANCZOS, *Applied Analysis*, Prentice-Hall, Englewood Cliffs, New Jersey, 1956.

J. A. SHOHAT and J. D. TAMARKIN, *The Problem of Moments*, Amer. Math. Soc., Providence, Rhode Island, 1943.

P. J. DAVIS, *Interpolation and Approximation*, Blaisdell, New York, 1963.

J. TODD (ed.), *Survey of Mathematical Analysis*, McGraw-Hill, New York, 1962.

§3. The classic work on orthogonal polynomials is

G. SZEGO, *Orthogonal Polynomials*, Amer. Math. Soc., Providence, Rhode Island, 1939.

See also

E. T. WHITTAKER and G. N. WATSON, *Modern Analysis*, Cambridge University Press, London, 1935.

For the evaluation of the determinant $|(a_i + a_j)^{-1}|$, see

G. POLYA and G. SZEGO, *Aufgaben und Lehratze aus der Analysis*, Dover Publications, New York, 1945, p. 98.

The Legendre polynomials arise in a very natural fashion in the study of potential theory in connection with the distance function $(1 - 2rx + x^2)^{-1/2}$. From this point of view, Rodrigues' formula is quite expected and may be derived from the Lagrange expansion formula, see

R. BELLMAN, *Perturbation Techniques in Mathematics, Physics, and Engineering*, Holt, Rinehart & Winston, New York, 1964.

§4. For some discussion of the efficiency of Horner's procedure, see

A. OSTROWSKI, "On Two Problems in Abstract Algebra Connected with Horner's Rule," *Studies in Mathematics and Mechanics*, Academic Press, New York, 1954, pp. 40–48.

Unpublished work in this area has been done by T. MOTZKIN.

§8. Our first systematic use of this inversion technique is given in

R. BELLMAN, H. KAGIWADA, R. KALABA, and M. PRESTRUD, *Invariant Imbedding and Time-Dependent Processes*, American Elsevier, New York, 1964.

§15. For an application of this technique, see

R. BELLMAN and R. KALABA, "A Note on Nonlinear Summability Techniques in Invariant Imbedding," *J. Math. Anal. Appl.*, Vol. 6, 1963, pp. 465–472.

H. RUTISHAUSER, "Der Quotienten-differenzen-algorithmus," *Z. Angew. Math. Physik*, Vol. 5, 1954, pp. 233–251.

D. SHANKS, "Nonlinear Transformations of Divergent and Slowly Convergent Sequences," *J. Math. Phys.*, Vol. 34, 1955, pp. 1–42.

§16. This follows

R. BELLMAN, *Numerical Solution of Functional Equations by Means of Laplace Transform—VII: Mellin Transform*, The RAND Corporation, RM-4179-NIH, July 1964.

§18. For an application of this technique, see

R. BELLMAN, H. KAGIWADA, and R. KALABA, "On a New Approach to the Numerical Solution of a Class of Partial Differential Integral Equations of Transport Theory," *Proc. Nat. Acad. Sci. USA*, Vol. 54, 1965, pp. 1293–1296.

R. BELLMAN, H. KAGIWADA, and R. KALABA, *Invariant Imbedding and Perturbation Techniques Applied to Diffuse Reflection from Spherical Shells*, The RAND Corporation, RM-4730-NASA, August 1965.

For a detailed discussion of a number of alternate inversion techniques with further references, see

T. L. COST, "Approximate Laplace Transform Inversions in Viscoelastic Stress Analysis," *AIAA Journal*, Vol. 2, 1964, pp. 2157–2166.

See also

H. V. NORDEN and I. SEPPA, "A Problem on Heat Conduction in a Wire Enclosed by a Cylindrical Material solved by Numerical Inverse Laplace Transform," *Nordisk Tidskrift for Informationsbehandling*, Vol. 4, 1964, pp. 224–242.

Chapter Three

LINEAR FUNCTIONAL EQUATIONS

I. INTRODUCTION

In this chapter, we wish to apply the numerical inversion techniques developed in the previous pages to obtain the computational solution of a number of the familiar and important equations of mathematical physics. Many of these equations play equally significant roles in a number of the other areas of applied mathematics. In particular, we shall discuss a problem arising in chemotherapy and a question arising in system identification. Here we restrict ourselves to linear functional equations, reserving the subsequent chapter for nonlinear equations.

To begin with, we treat some classes of equations which allow an immediate explicit analytic expression for the Laplace transform of the solution. In this category fall the renewal equation

$$(1.1) \qquad u(t) = f(t) + \int_0^t u(t - t_1)g(t_1)\,dt_1,$$

and systems of renewal equations

$$(1.2) \qquad u_i(t) = f_i(t) + \int_0^t \left(\sum_{j=1}^N g_{ij}(t - t_1)u_j(t_1) \right) dt_1,$$

$i = 1, 2, \ldots, N$, as well as the differential-difference equation

$$(1.3) \qquad u'(t) = \sum_{i=1}^N a_i u(t - t_i),$$

systems of such equations, and various combinations of these forms.

Closely related to the foregoing is the integral equation of Abel,

$$(1.4) \qquad f(t) = \int_0^t u(t - t_1)g(t_1)\,dt_1,$$

which crops up in such unexpected places. For example, we encounter

49

this equation in connection with the determination of the structure of a linear system given the inputs and outputs as functions of time. We treat a particular version of this problem using the successive approximation technique of the theory of quasilinearization.

Also treated is what appears to be a quite simple problem: Obtain the numerical solution of a linear differential equation of the form

$$(1.5) \qquad u^{(n)} + a_1 u^{(n-1)} + \cdots + a_n u = 0,$$

where the a_i are constant and the initial conditions are given, $u^{(i)}(0) = c_i$, $i = 0, 1, \ldots, n-1$. Ordinarily, this is completely routine. However, if the characteristic roots vary greatly in magnitude and if the initial values c_i are such that the solution contains only terms corresponding to the smaller characteristic roots, then surprising and frustrating difficulties can arise if a conventional algorithm is employed. We term these equations "mismatched." Our first experience with equations of this perverse nature was in the field of radiative transfer.

Next, we treat an equation of unconventional nature arising in a mathematical model of chemotherapy,

$$(1.6) \qquad r_p u_t = -u_y + k(u - v),$$

$$r_e v'(t) = k \int_0^1 u \, dy - kv,$$

where u depends on y and t and v is a function of t alone, subject to various boundary and initial conditions.

Finally, we consider the equation

$$(1.7) \qquad k(x) u_t = u_{xx},$$

with the initial condition $u(x,0) = g(x)$, and time-dependent boundary conditions, $u(0,t) = h_0(t)$, $u(1,t) = h_1(t)$. Here $L(u)$ satisfies an ordinary differential equation in x which requires numerical integration in general.

The over-all procedure is the same in all of these cases: a multistage computational procedure based upon the fact that the Laplace transform satisfies a more tractable equation than that defining u

and upon the fact that we can use the numerical values of $L(u)$ to find numerical values of u.

References are given at the end of the chapter both to original sources and to more detailed discussions of the various kinds of functional equations that appear.

2. THE SCALAR RENEWAL EQUATION

The equation

$$(2.1) \qquad u(t) = f(t) + \int_0^t u(t - t_1)g(t_1)\,dt_1$$

(called the "renewal equation" because of its origin in the study of the replacement of items that wear out over time) possesses a very elegant explicit analytic solution in terms of Laplace transforms. Writing, as usual,

$$(2.2) \qquad L(u) = \int_0^\infty e^{-st}u(t)\,dt,$$

with similar notation for the transforms of f and g, we obtain, using the result of Sec. 4 of Chapter One,

$$(2.3) \qquad L(u) = L(f) + L\left[\int_0^t u(t - t_1)g(t_1)\,dt_1\right]$$
$$= L(f) + L(u)L(g).$$

Hence,

$$(2.4) \qquad L(u) = \frac{L(f)}{1 - L(g)}\,.$$

Using this explicit representation, we can now readily determine $u(t)$ numerically using the procedure outlined in Chapter Two. As in all that follows, we refer the reader to various sources for a rigorous discussion of the procedure employed.

This equation, together with various analogues and extensions, plays an important role in the modern theory of stochastic processes, particularly in the theory of branching processes, where applications to cascade processes abound, and it occupies a central position in queuing theory and inventory theory.

3. SOME EXAMPLES

To test the method, we begin with some cases where the solution can be obtained analytically. Consider the equation

(3.1) $$u(t) = 1 + \int_0^t e^{-a(t-s)}u(s)\, ds,$$

for the two cases $a = 1$ and $a = 2$. For $a = 1$, the explicit solution is $u = 1 + t$; for $a = 2$, we have $u = 2 - e^{-t}$. In the two figures that follow, we see the results of using 3-, 5-, 7-, and 10-point quadrature formulas. (See Figs. 3.1 and 3.2.)

The excellent agreement for the case $a = 2$ and also the oscillation about the true solution for $a = 1$ are both to be noted. The reason for this last effect, and—even more important—a way of avoiding it, is discussed below in the treatment of the numerical solution of differential-difference equations.

Consider next the equation

(3.2) $$u(t) = e^{-at} + \int_0^t e^{-(t-t_1)^2}u(t_1)\, dt_1,$$

of some interest in operations research and branching processes. There is no simple explicit analytic solution for $u(t)$, which means that we must use "internal criticism" in comparing the numerical solution. The simplest procedure is to compare the results obtained using different quadrature formulas. Figures 3.3, 3.4, and 3.5 show the numerical solutions for the cases $a = 0, 1, 2$ using 3-, 5-, 7-, and 10-point quadrature formulas.

The total time required for twelve cases, consisting of three values of a, each with four quadrature formulas, was twenty seconds on an IBM-7090.

Observe once again the solution, for the case $a = 0$ appears to exhibit numerical instability, an illustration of the phenomenon occurring above in connection with equation (3.1) for $a = 1$. By "numerical instability" in this case, we mean a tendency to oscillate about the true solution. Observe that there is much less of this for $a = 2$. We shall return to this phenomenon in Secs. 7 and 8.

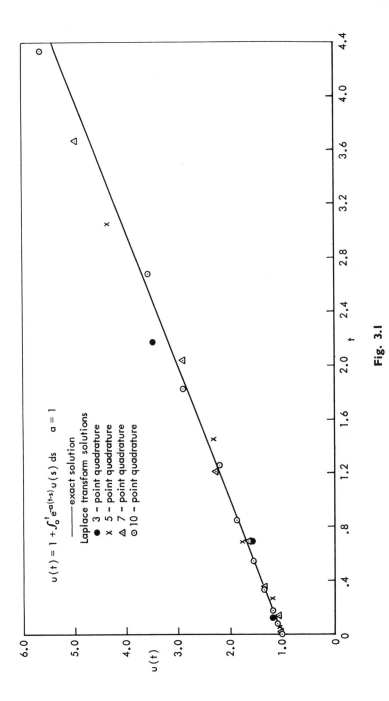

$$u(t) = 1 + \int_o^t e^{-a(t-s)} u(s)\, ds \qquad a = 1$$

——— exact solution

Laplace transform solutions
● 3 – point quadrature
× 5 – point quadrature
△ 7 – point quadrature
⊙ 10 – point quadrature

Fig. 3.1

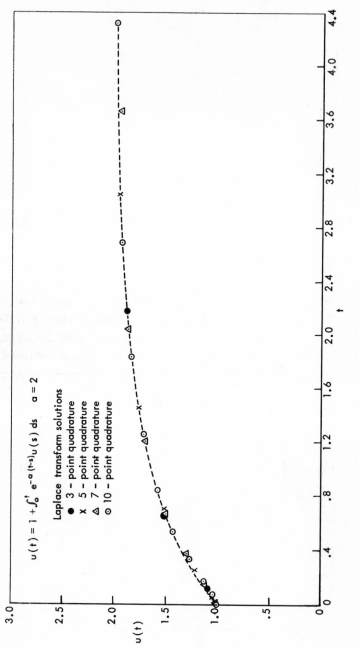

Fig. 3.2

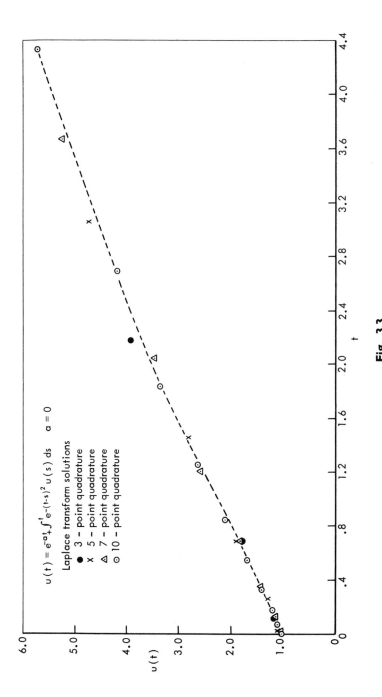

Fig. 3.3

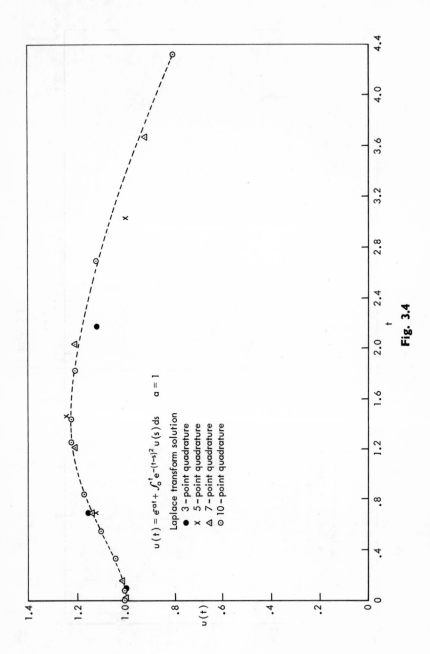

$$u(t) = e^{at} + \int_o^t e^{-(t-s)^2} u(s)\, ds \qquad a = 1$$

Laplace transform solution
● 3 - point quadrature
× 5 - point quadrature
△ 7 - point quadrature
⊙ 10 - point quadrature

Fig. 3.4

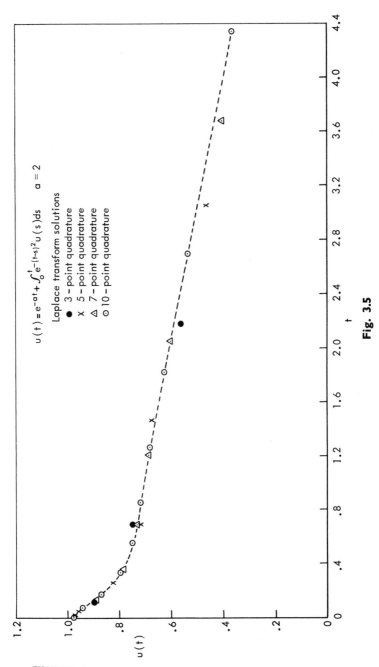

$$u(t) = e^{-at} + \int_o^t e^{-(t-s)^2} u(s)\,ds \qquad a = 2$$

Laplace transform solutions

● 3 – point quadrature
× 5 – point quadrature
△ 7 – point quadrature
⊙ 10 – point quadrature

Fig. 3.5

4. SYSTEMS OF RENEWAL EQUATIONS

Realistic versions of a number of processes in operations research and mathematical physics lead to systems of renewal equations,

$$(4.1) \quad u_i(t) = f_i(t) + \int_0^t \left[\sum_{j=1}^N g_{ij}(s) u_j(t - s) \right] ds, \qquad i = 1, 2, \ldots, N.$$

When treating a single equation of the type discussed above in (3.1), we have a choice of a variety of techniques since time and storage pressures are hardly acute. For a system of equations such as (4.1), however, with N large, say 10 or 20, the conventional approaches can be both time- and storage-consuming.*

Applying the Laplace transform, we have

$$(4.2) \qquad L(u_i) = L(f_i) + \sum_{j=1}^N L(g_{ij}) L(u_j).$$

Hence, to determine $L(u_i)$, we must solve a system of linear algebraic equations. Sometimes this can be done easily; in some cases, some effort is required. In what follows, we present an example where everything proceeds smoothly. In Chapter Five, we shall discuss some techniques to be employed upon recalcitrant linear algebraic equations. And it should be added parenthetically that no linear algebraic equation is to be considered above suspicion until proven so.

5. AN EXAMPLE

Let us consider the vector equation

$$(5.1) \qquad x(t) = f + \int_0^t K(t - s) x(s) \, ds,$$

* Naturally, these quaint concepts of "large," $N = 10$ or 20, will date the writing of this book almost more accurately than a publication date. What we mean, of course, is that no matter how large the computers available are, there will always be a need to use ingenuity and sophistication to treat the problems which are "large" by contemporary standards.

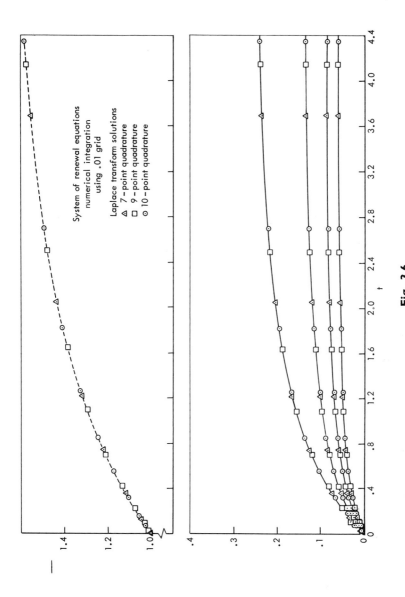

System of renewal equations
numerical integration
using .01 grid

Laplace transform solutions
△ 7 - point quadrature
□ 9 - point quadrature
⊙ 10 - point quadrature

Fig. 3.6

where the vector f and the matrix K are given respectively by

$$(5.2) \quad f = \begin{bmatrix} 1 \\ 0 \\ 0 \\ 0 \\ 0 \end{bmatrix}, \quad K(t) = \begin{bmatrix} \dfrac{e^{-t}}{3} & \dfrac{e^{-t}}{3} & 0 & 0 & 0 \\[2mm] \dfrac{e^{-2t}}{4} & \dfrac{e^{-2t}}{4} & \dfrac{e^{-2t}}{4} & 0 & 0 \\[2mm] \dfrac{e^{-3t}}{5} & \dfrac{e^{-3t}}{5} & \dfrac{e^{-3t}}{5} & \dfrac{e^{-3t}}{5} & 0 \\[2mm] \dfrac{e^{-4t}}{6} & \dfrac{e^{-4t}}{6} & \dfrac{e^{-4t}}{6} & \dfrac{e^{-4t}}{6} & \dfrac{e^{-4t}}{6} \\[2mm] \dfrac{e^{-5t}}{7} & \dfrac{e^{-5t}}{7} & \dfrac{e^{-5t}}{7} & \dfrac{e^{-5t}}{7} & \dfrac{e^{-5t}}{7} \end{bmatrix}.$$

These expressions were chosen so that (5.1) could be transformed, by differentiation, into an ordinary differential equation with initial values if we so wished. In this way, a very accurate solution can be obtained.

Quadrature formulas of degrees 7, 9, and 10 were used, and the mutual agreement was so excellent that we made no effort to determine the numerical solution of the equivalent differential equations for comparison purposes. The numerical results appear in Fig. 3.6.

6. DIFFERENTIAL-DIFFERENCE EQUATIONS

Let us now consider the differential-difference equation

$$(6.1) \qquad u'(t) = au(t) + bu(t - \lambda), \qquad t \geq 0,$$

$$u(t) = g(t), \qquad -\lambda \leq t \leq 0.$$

Note that the initial condition is now an interval condition, rather than a point condition. Applying the Laplace transform to both sides of (6.1), we readily obtain the explicit result

$$(6.2) \qquad L(u) = \frac{u(0) + be^{-\lambda s} \displaystyle\int_{-\lambda}^{0} e^{-rs} g(r)\, dr}{(s - a - be^{-\lambda s})}.$$

The integral

(6.3)
$$\int_{-\lambda}^{0} e^{-rs} g(r)\, dr$$

is to be evaluated numerically, by use of our usual quadrature formula, if $g(r)$ is not a function such as a polynomial or exponential polynomial for which it permits a simple explicit analytic evaluation.

7. A POOR EXAMPLE

To test the method, consider the simple equation

(7.1)
$$u'(t) = u(t-1), \qquad t \geq 0,$$
$$u(t) = 1, \qquad -1 \leq t \leq 0.$$

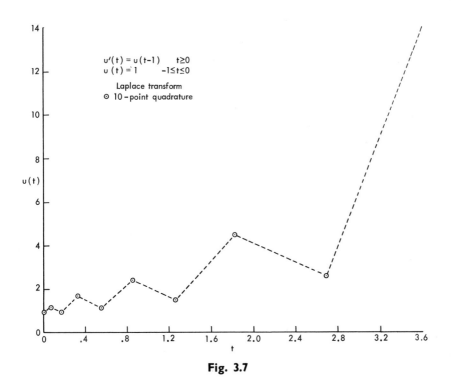

Fig. 3.7

It is easy to obtain the analytic representation of $u(t)$ over an interval such as $0 \leq t \leq 5$ by means of a step-by-step operation.

To our chagrin, the results obtained using our procedure extremely poor; even upon using a 10-point quadrature formula; see Fig. 3.7. This is a beautiful example of numerical instability! What is the explanation of this, and what can be done to obtain better results?

8. ASYMPTOTIC BEHAVIOR AND L^2-DIVERGENCE

Let us return to our change of variable, $e^{-t} = r$, which converts the relation $f(s) = L(u)$ into

$$(8.1) \qquad \int_0^1 r^{s-1} u \left(\log \frac{1}{r} \right) dr = f(s).$$

Setting $s = 1, 2, \ldots, N$ and using a quadrature formula of degree N is equivalent, as we have previously discussed, to the assumption that $u(\log 1/r)$ can be approximated by the first $(N + 1)$ terms of an expansion in terms of shifted Legendre polynomials,

$$u(\log 1/r) \cong \sum_{k=0}^{N} a_k P_k^*(r).$$

We determine the coefficients a_k in this truncated orthogonal expansion by the condition that the expression

$$(8.2) \qquad \int_0^1 \left(u \left(\log \frac{1}{r} \right) - \sum_{k=0}^{N} a_k P_k^*(r) \right)^2 dr$$

is to be minimized. Clearly, a minimal requirement that this approximation be acceptable is that the integral in (8.2) exists. This requires that

$$(8.3) \qquad \int_0^1 \left[u \left(\log \frac{1}{r} \right) \right]^2 dr < \infty.$$

Furthermore, since each $P_k^*(r)$, as a polynomial, is finite at $r = 0$, we would expect that closeness of fit, according to any criterion, would be considerably enhanced by having $u(\log 1/r)$ finite at $r = 0$.

Let us now return to the equation

(8.4) $$u'(t) = u(t - 1).$$

Since this is a linear equation with constant coefficients, it is logical, in view of our experience with ordinary differential equations, to look for a particular solution of the form $e^{\lambda t}$. Substituting $e^{\lambda t}$ in (8.4), we see that there is a solution of this type for every λ which is a root of the characteristic equation

(8.5) $$\lambda = e^{-\lambda}.$$

Standard results in the theory of functions of a complex variable allow us to demonstrate that this equation has an infinite number of roots λ_i, $i = 1, 2, \ldots$. We would expect then that we can write the general solution in the form

(8.6) $$u(t) = \sum_{i=1}^{\infty} c_i e^{\lambda_i t}.$$

This is indeed so in a number of cases, although not an easy matter to establish. It is, however, of no import for what concerns us here.

Let us suppose that we arrange the roots in order of decreasing real part so that

(8.7) $$Re(\lambda_1) \geq Re(\lambda_2) \geq Re(\lambda_3) \geq \cdots.$$

If there is one root λ_1 with largest real part, the asymptotic behavior of $u(t)$ as $t \to \infty$ is determined by the term

$$c_1 e^{\lambda_1 t}.$$

This may be established, using the contour integral representation for the solution of (8.4), starting from the explicit representation for $L(u)$ given in (6.2). The details are given in Sec. 10 below.

Assuming that this is the case, let us observe a consequence of this fact. If

(8.8) $$u(t) \sim c_1 e^{\lambda_1 t}$$

as $t \to \infty$, then

(8.9) $$u\left(\log \frac{1}{r}\right) \sim c_1 r^{-\lambda_1},$$

as $r \to 0$. Hence, if $Re\ (\lambda_1) > 0$, we see that $u(\log 1/r)$ is infinite at $r = 0$. As mentioned above, this militates against ordinary point convergence and, at very least, against uniform convergence. Furthermore, if $Re\ (\lambda_1) > \frac{1}{2}$, the integral

$$(8.10) \qquad \int_0^1 u^2 \left(\log \frac{1}{r} \right) dr = \infty,$$

and thus, not even mean-square convergence can hold. By this we mean that we cannot even expect that a sequence of coefficients $\{a_k\}$ exists such that

$$(8.11) \qquad \lim_{N \to \infty} \int_0^1 \left[u \left(\log \frac{1}{r} \right) - \sum_{k=0}^N a_k P_k^*(r) \right]^2 dr = 0.$$

Thus, from all points of view, we have no reason to suspect that we would get much useful information from the quadrature formula or that the solution of the linear system of algebraic equations would yield an approximation to values of $u(t)$.

Despite all of this, there is a very simple way out of our difficulties, as we shall see in Sec. 12.

9. THE EQUATION $\lambda = e^{-\lambda}$

Let us begin by establishing the fact that the equation

$$(9.1) \qquad \lambda = e^{-\lambda}$$

has precisely one real root which is positive and larger than $\frac{1}{2}$. (This root, λ_1, is approximately 0.5671, but the indicated accuracy is not required for our subsequent discussion.)

The existence of one real positive root is easily seen in Fig. 3.8. Observe that

$$(9.2) \qquad \tfrac{1}{2} e^{\frac{1}{2}} - 1 < \frac{1.7}{2} - 1 < 0,$$

and $e - 1 > 0$. Hence, if $f(\lambda) = \lambda - e^{-\lambda}$, we see that $f(\frac{1}{2}) < 0$, $f(1) > 0$. Hence, there is a root of (9.1) between $\frac{1}{2}$ and 1.

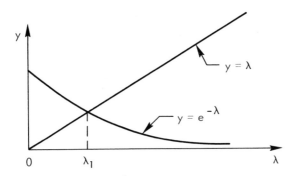

Fig. 3.8

For completeness, let us show that λ_1 is the root of (9.1) with largest real part. If $\lambda = x + iy$ is another root, with $x > 0$ and $y \neq 0$, we have

$$(9.3) \qquad\qquad x + iy = e^{-(x+iy)},$$

thus $x < |x + iy| = e^{-x}$. Hence, $x - e^{-x} < 0$, whence $x < \lambda_1$. We already know that there are no other real roots.

If we wish to determine the numerical values of the complex roots of $\lambda = e^{-\lambda}$, we use the foregoing equation and equate real and complex parts,

$$(9.4) \qquad\qquad x = e^{-x} \cos y,$$

$$y = e^{-x} \sin y,$$

whence

$$(9.5) \qquad\qquad \frac{\sin y}{y} = e^{\frac{y \cos y}{\sin y}}.$$

From this, plotting both sides, we can readily obtain numerical bounds and asymptotic behavior as the roots increase in magnitude.

10. RIGOROUS PROOF OF ASYMPTOTIC BEHAVIOR

To establish the asymptotic relation

$$(10.1) \qquad\qquad u(t) \sim c_1 e^{\lambda_1 t} \qquad \text{as} \quad t \to \infty$$

for the solution of (7.1), in a rigorous fashion, we use the explicit inversion formula given in Sec. 5 of Chapter One.

Using (6.2), we know that

$$(10.2) \qquad L(u) = \frac{\left(1 + e^{-s}\int_{-1}^{0} e^{-rs}\, dr\right)}{(s - e^{-s})}$$

$$= \frac{1 + \dfrac{1 - e^{-s}}{s}}{s - e^{-s}} = \frac{(s + 1 - e^{-s})}{s(s - e^{-s})}.$$

Hence, we can write

$$(10.3) \qquad u = \frac{1}{2\pi i}\int_{C} \frac{e^{st}(s + 1 - e^{-s})\, ds}{s(s - e^{-s})},$$

where C is the line $1 + i\tau$, $-\infty < \tau < \infty$. (See Fig. 3.9.) Shifting the line of integration to the left to C' (where C' can be taken to be the line $\frac{1}{2} + i\tau$, $-\infty < \tau < \infty$), past the line $Re\,(s) = \lambda_1$, we obtain a contribution

$$(10.4) \qquad c_1 e^{\lambda_1 t},$$

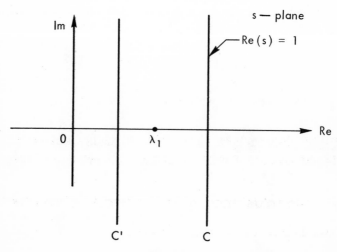

Fig. 3.9

due to the zero $s = \lambda_1$ of the denominator $s - e^{-s}$, where

(10.5) $c_1 = \dfrac{1}{\lambda_1(1 + e^{-\lambda_1})} \neq 0.$

It is not difficult to show that the contribution from the contour integral along C' is of smaller order of magnitude than

$$e^{\lambda_1 t}$$

In this case it is bounded by an expression of the form $be^{\frac{t}{2}}$. The actual order of magnitude depends on λ_2, as given by (8.7). This establishes the desired asymptotic behavior. The details of investigations of this type are given in books cited in the references.

11. NUMERICAL UTILITY OF ASYMPTOTIC BEHAVIOR

We have gone into this matter of asymptotic behavior for several reasons. In the first place, we wanted to explain the origin of the strange oscillations in the numerical solution which show up in some problems and not in others. In carrying out large-scale computations, it is essential to know what is going on. Surprises are unpleasant!

Second, we wish to indicate how we might supplement the set of values $\{u(t_i)\}$ which we obtain via numerical inversion based on quadrature. We pointed out in Sec. 13 of Chapter Two that even for large N (of the order of magnitude of 15), the largest t_i value is only 5.115. This is quite unsatisfactory in many situations. Hence, it is important to possess simple techniques for finding approximate values of $u(t)$ for much larger t-values. These asymptotic values will also furnish a valuable check on the values of $\{u(t_i)\}$ obtained by means of numerical inversion.

Finally, let us note that the same technique as that sketched in Sec. 10 permits us to obtain the asymptotic behavior of the more general equations appearing in (1.1) to (1.4), as well as those treated in subsequent sections.

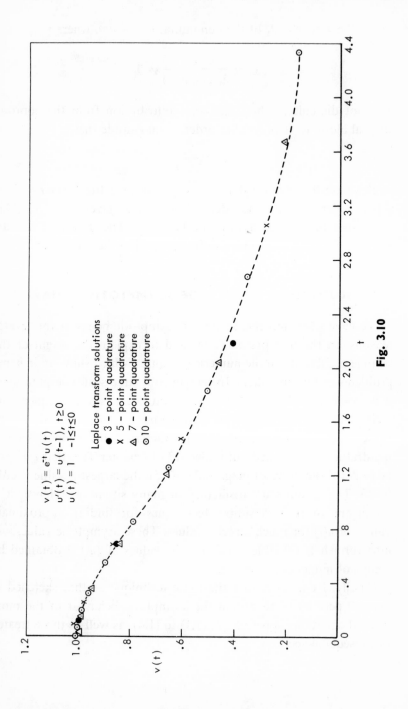

Fig. 3.10

12. A SIMPLE REMEDY

There is a very simple and efficient technique for avoiding the computational difficulties observed in Sec. 7. Consider the differential-difference equation satisfied by $v = e^{-t}u$. We have

(12.1) $$\frac{d}{dt}(e^t v(t)) = e^{(t-1)}v(t-1),$$

or

(12.2) $$v'(t) + v(t) = e^{-1}v(t-1).$$

From what we have deduced concerning the behavior of $u(t)$ as $t \to \infty$, we know that at $r = 0$,

(12.3) $$v\left(\log\frac{1}{r}\right) = 0.$$

Alternatively, and much simpler in practice, we invert the relation

(12.4) $$L(v) = f(s+1),$$

in place of $L(u) = f(s)$, since

(12.5) $$L(ue^{-t}) = \int_0^\infty e^{-t}u(t)e^{-st}\,dt = f(s+1).$$

In Fig. 3.10 we give the values obtained in this fashion for $v(t)$, and in Fig. 3.11, those for $u(t)$ derived by performing the multiplication $u(t) = e^t v(t)$.

13. MISMATCHED EQUATIONS

Let us now consider what appears to be a most elementary and routine computational problem. We wish to determine the numerical solution of the linear differential equation

(13.1) $$u^{(4)} - 22u^{(3)} + 39u^{(2)} + 22u^{(1)} - 40u = 0,$$

subject to the initial conditions

(13.2) $$u(0) = 1, \quad u'(0) = -1, \quad u^{(2)}(0) = 1, \quad u^{(3)}(0) = -1.$$

This is an ordinary differential equation with prescribed initial value conditions. Where could a difficulty lurk?

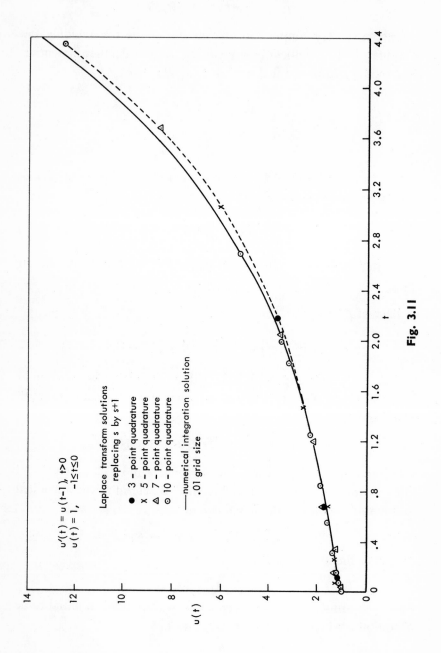

Fig. 3.11

The roots of the characteristic equation

(13.3) $\lambda^4 - 22\lambda^3 + 39\lambda^2 + 22\lambda - 40 = 0$

are $\lambda = -1, 1, 2, 20$, which means that the *general* solution of (13.1) is

(13.4) $u = c_1 e^{-t} + c_2 e^t + c_3 e^{2t} + c_4 e^{20t}.$

The initial conditions given above have been malevolently chosen so that

(13.5) $u(t) = e^{-t}$

is the solution of (13.1) plus (13.2). What we wish to show is that

(13.6) $1 + 2 \neq 5,$

by which we mean that (13.1) and (13.2), combined in the usual computational manner, do not yield a solution agreeing with (13.5).

If we employ integration routines, we encounter strange effects. Figure 3.12 shows the result of a numerical integration using an Adams-Moulton method with a grid size of 0.01. What has happened?

The answer is very simple. When we integrate numerically, we introduce small errors in the values of $u(t)$. This means that we unconsciously allow a solution of the general form given in (13.4) to enter,

(13.7) $u_e(t) = e^{-t} + \epsilon_1 e^t + \epsilon_2 e^{2t} + \epsilon_3 e^{20t},$

where ϵ_1, ϵ_2, and ϵ_3 are presumably small quantities. The terms e^t and e^{2t} will not cause much trouble for a while, but since

(13.8) $e^{10} \simeq 10^{4.33}, \qquad e^{20} \simeq 10^{8.66},$

we see that even if $\epsilon_3 = 10^{-6}$, we can expect a "blow-up" for medium size t, and this is indeed what occurs.

We must guard against this phenomenon whenever the characteristic roots vary greatly in magnitude. There is no guaranteed

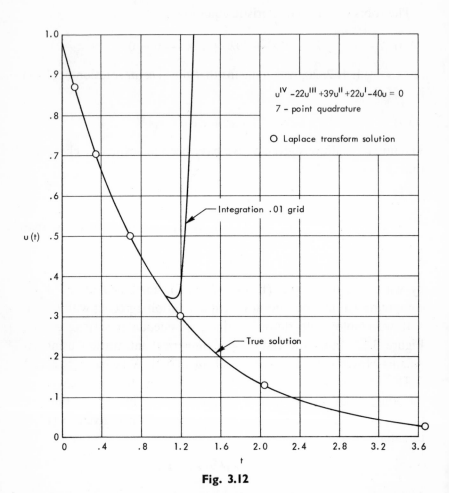

Fig. 3.12

preventive, and the situation is quite similar to what we face in treating an ill-conditioned system of linear algebraic equations.

In the following section, we indicate how the Laplace transform may be used to overcome, or better yet circumvent, the difficulty in this case.*

* There is an old European folk proverb to the effect that it is easier to avoid the devil than to wrestle with him.

14. LAPLACE TRANSFORM SOLUTION

To use the Laplace transform in a simple fashion, let us convert (13.1) into a first order system,

$$(14.1) \qquad \begin{aligned} u_1' &= u_2, & u_1(0) &= 1, \\ u_2' &= u_3, & u_2(0) &= -1, \\ u_3' &= u_4, & u_3(0) &= 1, \\ u_4' &= 22u_4 - 39u_3 - 22u_2 + 40u_1, & u_4(0) &= -1. \end{aligned}$$

Taking Laplace transforms and setting $w_i = L(u_i)$, $i = 1, 2, 3, 4$, we have

$$(14.2) \qquad \begin{aligned} sw_1 &= w_2 + 1, \\ sw_2 &= w_3 - 1, \\ sw_3 &= w_4 + 1, \\ sw_4 &= 22w_4 - 39w_3 - 22w_2 + 40w_1 + 1. \end{aligned}$$

If we solved this linear system explicitly by means of determinants, we would find, of course, that

$$(14.3) \qquad w_1 = \frac{P_1(s)}{P_2(s)} = \frac{1}{s + 1}.$$

In general, however, when this equation arises as part of a comprehensive mathematical formulation, we expect to solve (14.2) numerically for $s = 1, 2, \ldots, N$, using any of a number of standard algorithms for solving linear systems of algebraic equations.

This direct procedure leads to difficulties in this case since $P_2(s)$ vanishes at $s = 1$ and 2. These zeros are canceled analytically by corresponding zeros of the numerator, but not necessarily numerically. To avoid this small pitfall, we use an alternate set of s-values, namely, $s = \frac{3}{2}, \frac{5}{2}, \frac{7}{2}, \ldots, \frac{1}{2} + R$.

In a general case of high dimensionality where we might not want to take time to determine characteristic roots, we could use the values $\{a + k\}$, $k = 1, 2, \ldots, R$, for several random values of a to ensure

that this difficulty is avoided. The time required for the entire process
is so short that we can afford this simple-minded approach.

In Fig. 3.12 we presented a graph of e^{-t} and indicated the values
obtained by solving (14.2) numerically and then inverting numerically.

In Fig. 3.13, we see corresponding results for the equation

(14.4) $u^{(4)} - 12u^{(3)} + 19u^{(2)} + 12u^{(1)} - 20u = 0,$

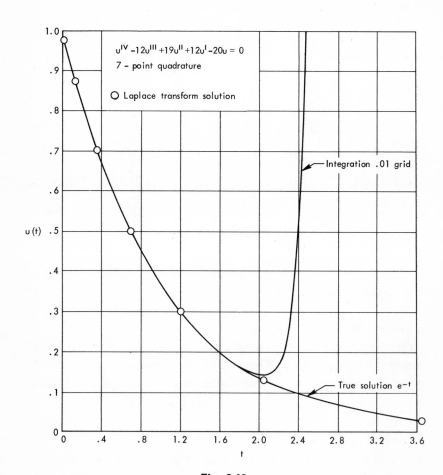

Fig. 3.13

with $u(0) = 1$, $u'(0) = -1$, $u^{(2)}(0) = 1$, $u^{(3)}(0) = -1$, and $u = e^{-t}$ again a solution.

If we wish to continue the solution far out in time, we can either use the techniques discussed in Sec. 13 of Chapter Two or use the fact that $w(t) = u(t + t_0)$ is a solution of the linear differential equation satisfying the new initial conditions

$$(14.5) \qquad w(0) = u(t_0), \qquad w'(0) = u'(t_0), \qquad w^{(2)}(0) = u^{(2)}(t_0),$$
$$w^{(3)}(0) = u^{(3)}(t_0).$$

We thus start over again with a solution for $w(t)$ by means of the Laplace transform.

Finally, we could use the asymptotic form of $u(t)$, as $t \to \infty$, which, in this case, can be determined by elementary means.

15. THE ONE-DIMENSIONAL HEAT EQUATION

Let us now turn our attention to a partial differential equation where the merit of the Laplace transform resides in converting it into an ordinary differential equation. The equation is

$$(15.1) \qquad k(x)u_t = u_{xx},$$

subject to the initial and boundary conditions

$$(15.2) \qquad u(x,0) = g(x), \qquad 0 < x < 1,$$
$$u(0,t) = h_1(t), \qquad u(1,t) = h_2(t), \qquad t > 0.$$

This equation may be considered to arise in the following fashion. Take a slender rod of cross-section area A and of length L. Let its mass per unit length be ρ, its specific heat be c, and its conductivity be k_1. We denote the temperature at a point x from the left end of the rod at time t by $u(x,t)$, and we symbolize the amount of heat per unit cross-section area per unit time passing x to the right at time t by $F(x,t)$. We focus our attention on the cylinder of base area A extending from x to $x + \Delta$. On the one hand, the rate at which heat is being supplied to it is $c\rho\Delta Au_t$. On the other hand, it is $A[F(x, t) - F(x + \Delta,t)]$. Thus,

$$(15.3) \qquad\qquad c\rho\,\Delta Au_t = -AF_x\Delta,$$

where we have dropped all terms involving powers of Δ higher than the first. In addition, a basic heat conduction postulate is

$$(15.4) \qquad\qquad F = -k_1 u_x.$$

These equations lead to the desired heat equation,

$$(15.5) \qquad\qquad k(x)u_t = u_{xx},$$

where we have set

$$(15.6) \qquad\qquad k(x) = \rho c/k_1.$$

We have written $k(x)$ to emphasize that the rod may be inhomogeneous with its density a function of position.

Equations of this type also arise in the study of random walk and diffusion processes.

We shall suppose that $\infty \geq \delta_2 \geq k(x) \geq \delta_1 > 0$ for $0 \leq x \leq 1$. Although much weaker conditions are sufficient, this simple condition is appropriate here.

If $k(x)$ is a function of general form, this equation cannot be solved explicitly in terms of the elementary functions of analysis. If numerical results are desired, recourse must be had to computational algorithms. Of these, difference methods are most prominent at the moment. We shall pursue an entirely different approach based upon the use of the Laplace transform.

This problem is a bit more complex than those heretofore treated since we have neither an explicit expression for the Laplace transform, nor do we have an initial value problem to solve. Here, as we shall see in a moment in our use of the Laplace transform, we face a two-point, boundary-value problem—fortunately, with an associated linear ordinary differential equation.

The technique, in principle, is applicable to high-order parabolic equations such as

$$(15.7) \qquad\qquad k(x,y)u_t = u_{xx} + u_{yy}.$$

However, since the calculations for equations of this type can consume an appreciable time, we beg the reader's indulgence and ask him to follow our precept rather than our example.

16. THE TRANSFORM EQUATION

Applying the Laplace transform to (15.1), we obtain the equation

$$(16.1) \qquad v'' - sk(x)v = -k(x)g(x), \qquad 0 < x < 1,$$

with the boundary conditions

$$(16.2) \qquad v(0) = H_1(s), \qquad v(1) = H_2(s),$$

where

$$(16.3) \qquad v \equiv v(x,s) = L(u),$$
$$H_1(s) = L(h_1), \qquad H_2(s) = L(h_2).$$

In (16.1), the prime denotes differentiation with respect to x.

The two-point, boundary-value problem is solved numerically for each value of s we use, in the usual fashion which we now describe. Let $v_1(x)$ and $v_2(x)$ (suppressing the explicit dependence on s) be determined respectively as the solutions of

$$(16.4) \qquad v_1'' - sk(x)v_1 = -k(x)g(x), \qquad v_1(0) = 1, \qquad v_1'(0) = 0,$$
$$v_2'' - sk(x)v_2 = 0, \qquad\qquad v_2(0) = 0, \qquad v_2'(0) = 1.$$

These are the so-called principal solutions. Returning to (16.1), set

$$(16.5) \qquad v = H_1(s)v_1 + av_2,$$

where a is a constant to be determined using the second condition in (16.2). Then, the condition at $x = 1$ yields

$$(16.6) \qquad H_2(s) = H_1(s)v_1(1) + av_2(1).$$

The condition imposed upon $k(x)$ ensures that $v_2(1) \neq 0$. We ask the reader to accept this fact. These matters, which are neither simple nor elementary, are discussed at length in various references cited at the end of the chapter. Thus, we have for a the value

$$(16.7) \qquad a = \frac{H_2(s) - H_1(s)v_1(1)}{v_2(1)},$$

which via (16.5) determines the function $v(x)$.

17. SOME NUMERICAL RESULTS

The method was tested for the cases

(17.1) $$k(x) = 4, 9, 16,$$

with the initial condition

(17.2) $$u(x,0) = \sin \pi x.$$

These were chosen so that we could obtain simple explicit solutions

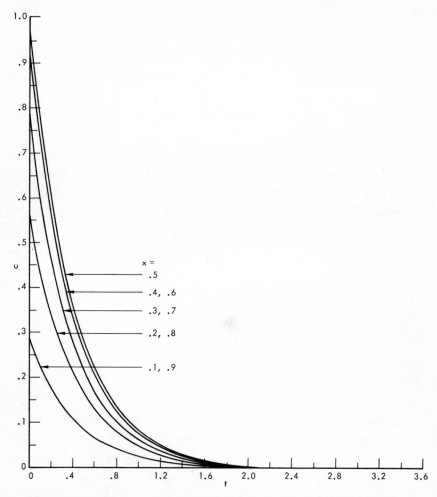

Fig. 3.14—Computational solution for $k(x) \equiv 4$, $g(x) = \sin \pi x$, using a seven-point quadrature formula

to test the accuracy of our procedure. If $k(x) = k^2$, a constant, the solution of (15.1) is given by

$$(17.3) \qquad\qquad u(x,t) = e^{-\frac{\pi^2 t}{k^2}} \sin \pi x,$$

as is immediately verified. We used a seven-point quadrature formula and obtained the results indicated in Figs. 3.14, 3.15, and

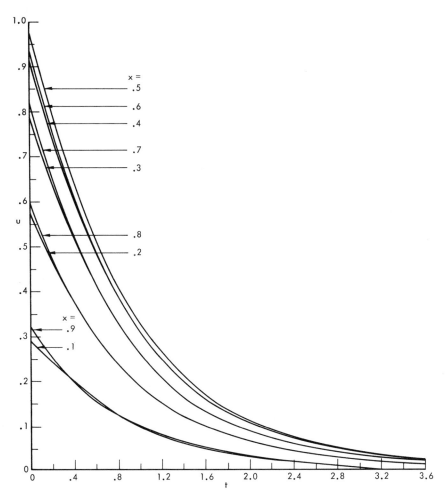

Fig. 3.15—Computational solution for $k(x) \equiv 9$, $g(x) = \sin \pi x$, using a seven-point quadrature formula

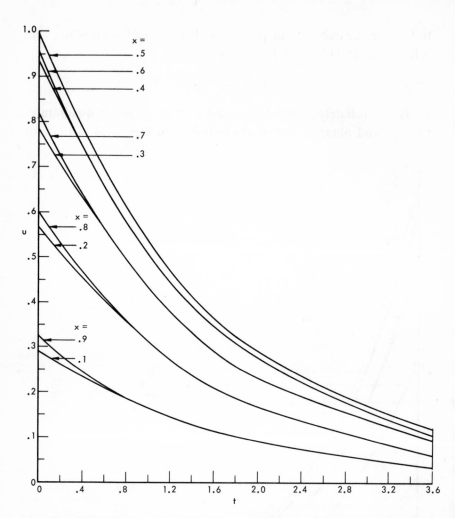

**Fig. 3.16—Computational solution for $k(x) \equiv 16$, $g(x) = \sin \pi x$,
using a seven-point quadrature formula**

3.16. The larger the value of k, the smaller the conductivity, and the slower the convergence to zero.

Figures 3.17 and 3.18 show the results for an inhomogeneous rod for which

$$(17.4) \qquad\qquad k(x) = 1 + x.$$

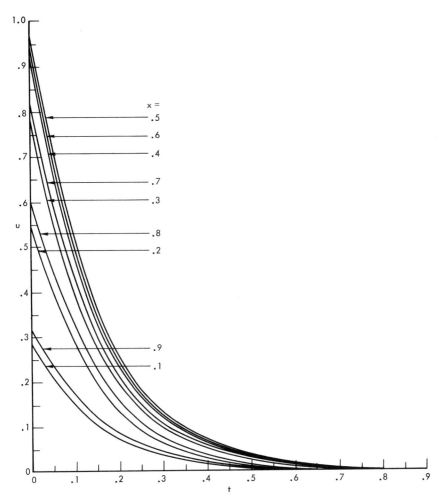

Fig. 3.17—Computational solution for $k(x) \equiv 1 + x$, $g(x) = \sin \pi x$,
using a seven-point quadrature formula

Here we have no simple explicit solution. The calculations were done with both seven- and nine-point quadrature formulas in order to obtain a self-consistent check on the accuracy.

The production of the data for one of the graphs took about

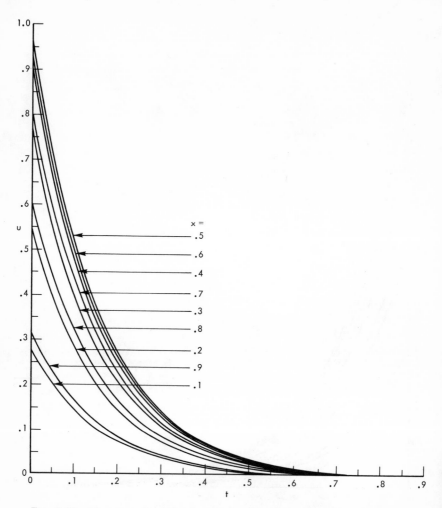

Fig. 3.18—Computational solution for $k(x) \equiv 1 + x$, $g(x) = \sin \pi x$, using a nine-point quadrature formula

thirty seconds on an IBM-7090. In the integration of (16.4) and (16.5), a Runge-Kutta procedure with a grid size of 0.01 was used.

18. A CHEMOTHERAPY MODEL

Let us now turn to some more complicated equations arising out of a simplified version of physiological processes connected with chemotherapy. The equations are

(18.1) $$r_p u_t = -u_y + k(v - u),$$

$$r_e v'(t) = k \int_0^1 u \, dy - kv,$$

for $t > 0$, $0 < y < 1$. Here v depends only on t, while u depends on y and t. The initial conditions are

(18.2) $$u(y,0) = 0,$$

and the boundary conditions are

(18.3) $$u(0,t) = u_0, \qquad\qquad 0 < t < t_1,$$
$$= 0, \qquad\qquad t_1 < t \leq T,$$
$$= u(1, t - T), \qquad t > T.$$

This last condition corresponds to the fact that the blood requires a nonzero time to circulate.

There are several interesting features to this equation, such as the integral term, $\int_0^1 u \, dy$, and the time-lag in the boundary conditions.

Writing

(18.4) $$L(u) = U, \qquad L(v) = V$$

(and, as before, suppressing the explicit dependence of u on y), we obtain the system

(18.5) $$r_p s U = -U_y + k(V - U),$$

$$r_e s V = k \int_0^1 U(y,s) \, dy - kV.$$

The boundary condition of (18.3) becomes

(18.6) $$U(0,s) = \frac{u_0}{s}(1 - e^{-st_1}) + e^{-Ts}U(1,s).$$

19. EXPLICIT SOLUTION FOR $U(y,s)$

To obtain explicit analytic representations for U and V, we proceed as follows. Eliminating V, we see that U satisfies the integro-differential equation

(19.1) $$U_y + (sr_p + k)U - \frac{k^2}{sr_e + k} \int_0^1 U(y,s)\, dy = 0,$$

subject to the boundary conditions of (18.6).

To solve for U, we first regard this as an equation of the form

(19.2) $$U_y + (sr_p + k)U - \frac{k^2 m}{sr_e + k} = 0,$$

where m is a constant. Having done this, we set

(19.3) $$m = \int_0^1 U(y,s)\, dy,$$

to determine its value.

In this way, we find, after some elementary but tedious calculations that

(19.4) $$U(y,s) = \frac{\left[\dfrac{u_0}{s}(1 - e^{-st_1})\right]\left[e^{-ay} + \dfrac{b(1 - e^{-a})}{a(a - b)}\right]}{\left[(1 - e^{-sT-a}) + \dfrac{b(1 - e^{-sT})(1 - e^{-a})}{a(a - b)}\right]},$$

where

(19.5) $$a = sr_p + k, \qquad b = \frac{k^2}{(sr_e + k)},$$

$$a - b = \frac{s^2 r_e r_p + ks(r_e + r_p)}{sr_e + k}.$$

From this representation, we readily determine m, as given by (19.3) and then V from (18.5).

20. NUMERICAL RESULTS

Plausible values for r_p, r_e, k, t_1, T and u_0 are the following:

(20.1)
$$r_p = 3 \times 10^3,$$
$$r_e = 1 \times 10^4,$$
$$k = \tfrac{1000}{3},$$
$$t_1 = 0.3 \times 10^3,$$
$$T = (1.5) \times 10^3,$$
$$u_0 = 1 \times 10^3.$$

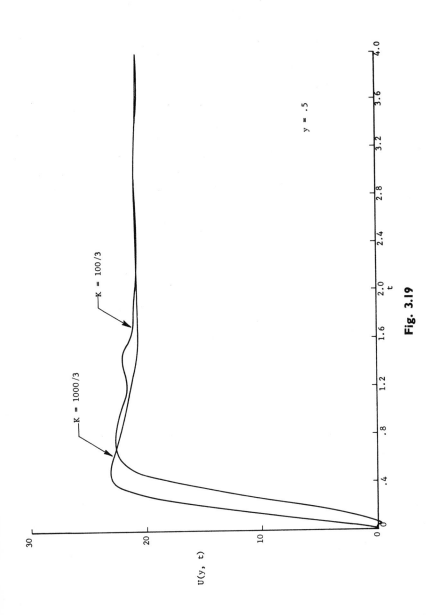

Fig. 3.19

In the above figure (Fig. 3.19), we give the results of seven and nine quadrature point calculations for the particular point $y = 0.5$. In view of the scales of the foregoing parameters, we changed the s-scale from units of 1 to units of 0.001.

21. INVERSE PROBLEMS

So far, we have considered a variety of physical processes which give rise to functional equations whose solution could be materially simplified by use of the Laplace transform. In some situations, however, it is not so much a matter of determining the solution as it is of determining the structure of the equation.

Let us consider a simple way in which a problem of this type can arise. Suppose that we are experimenting with a system we know can be described by means of the linear differential equation

$$(21.1) \qquad u'' + au' + bu = f(t),$$

where a and b are system parameters which are fixed, but unknown. Suppose further that we can measure the input $f(t)$ at various times, and likewise the output $u(t)$ at various times. At what times should the measurements be made, and how do we determine a and b?

Using the standard representation for the solution of an inhomogeneous equation as a function of the forcing term, we see that this is a particular version of the more general problem of determining the transfer function $k(t)$, given various properties of the input and output functions, $f(t)$ and $u(t)$, respectively, in the relation

$$(21.2) \qquad u(t) = \int_0^t k(t - s)f(s) \, ds.$$

This, in turn, is a particular version of the "black box" identification problem. Given a system S, a set of possible inputs and a set of sensing devices for outputs, we wish to determine the structure of S, missing values of outputs and inputs, and also what kinds of inputs to use to gain this information in systematic and efficient

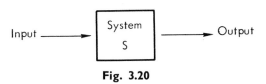

Fig. 3.20

fashions. A particularly important realization of this abstract identification process is medical diagnosis, and there are countless other realizations in economics, engineering, geophysics, astrophysics, and many other branches of modern science. (See Fig. 3.20.)

Frequently, the system S is composed of many linked subsystems, as in Fig. 3.21. Our objective here is to determine the properties of

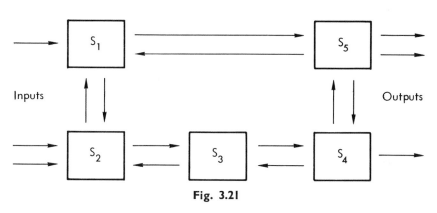

Fig. 3.21

S_3 by means of observations of the indirect inputs and outputs. There are many difficult and intriguing mathematical problems in this area. A different and more general numerical approach to questions of this type has been given in the previous volume in this series. Here we wish to indicate how the Laplace transform can be employed.

22. ESTIMATION OF SYSTEM CONSTANTS AND UNOBSERVABLE STATES

Consider the second-order linear system

$$(22.1) \qquad u'' + au' + bu = f(t).$$

We observe the values

(22.2) $u(t_i) = b_i,$ $i = 1, 2, \ldots, N,$

$$f(t_i) = f_i,$$

where the t_i are as above, namely,

$$e^{-t_i} = r_i,$$

and the initial displacement is $u(0) = c_0$. The value c_1 is unknown.

Using these values we wish to estimate the unknown system parameters a and b and the unknown initial velocity $u'(0) = c_1$. Taking Laplace transforms, we find

(22.3) $s^2 L - c_0 s - c_1 + a(sL - c_0) + bL = F(s),$

or

(22.4) $L(s) = \dfrac{F(s) + c_0 s + c_1 + a c_0}{s^2 + as + b}.$

On the other hand, we can use the observations at the times t_i to determine $L_{\text{Obs}}(s)$ for $s = 1, 2, \ldots, N$, via the familiar quadrature formula

(22.5) $L_{\text{Obs}}(s) = \displaystyle\sum_{i=1}^{N} r_i^{s-1} u(t_i) w_i,$

with a similar formula for $F_{\text{Obs}}(s)$ in terms of $f(t_i)$. We now wish to choose the constants a, b, and c_1, so as to make the theoretical Laplace transform $L(s)$ agree with the transform $L_{\text{Obs}}(s)$ obtained from the measurements of $u(t)$ and $f(t)$ as closely as possible in the sense of the method of least squares. That is, we wish to minimize the sum

(22.6) $S = \displaystyle\sum_{s=1}^{N} \{(s^2 + as + b)L_{\text{Obs}}(s) - [F(s) + c_0 s + c_1 + a c_0]\}^2,$

over-all a, b, and c_1. This expression is quadratic in a, b, and c_1; the minimizing values are to be determined as the solution of the simultaneous system of linear algebraic equations

(22.7) $\dfrac{\partial S}{\partial a} = \dfrac{\partial S}{\partial b} = \dfrac{\partial S}{\partial c_1} = 0.$

This is readily carried out. We give an example of this technique below.

23. NUMERICAL EXAMPLE

Consider the system

(23.1) $\ddot{u} + 3\dot{u} + 2u = 0,$ $u(0) = 3,$ $\dot{u}(0) = -4.$

The solution is

(23.2) $u(t) = e^{-2t} + 2e^{-t},$

and

(23.3) $u(3.6712) = 0.051539589$

$u(2.0461) = 0.27517036$

$u(1.2138) = 0.68240985$

$u(0.6931) = 1.2500000$

$u(0.3525) = 1.8999454$

$u(0.1384) = 2.4997639$

$u(0.0258) = 2.8988633.$

These are the appropriate values for use of a quadrature formula of order $N = 7$.

Starting with the foregoing values, and with the value $c_0 = 3$, and using the method described above, we found

$$a \cong 2.9968$$

$$b \cong 1.9961$$

$$c_1 \cong -3.9999.$$

The computing time on an IBM-7044 is negligible.

24. A MORE GENERAL IDENTIFICATION PROCESS

Let us consider the more general problem mentioned above in Sec. 22. Given values of the input $f(t)$ and the output $u(t)$, we wish to determine the structure of the system as characterized by the function $k(t)$ in

(24.1) $u(t) = \int_0^t k(t - t_1) f(t_1)\, dt_1.$

Using the Laplace transform, we can write

(24.2) $$L(k) = \frac{L(u)}{L(f)}.$$

Hence, if we agree to measure $u(t)$ and $f(t)$ at the quadrature points $\{t_i\}$, $i = 1, 2, \ldots, N$, we can evaluate the right-hand side of (24.2) by means of the expression

(24.3) $$\frac{\displaystyle\sum_{i=1}^{N} w_i u(t_i) e^{-st_i}}{\displaystyle\sum_{i=1}^{N} w_i f(t_i) e^{-st_i}} = L(k).$$

Using our inversion formula, we have an explicit relation

(24.4) $$k(t_i) = \sum_{j=1}^{N} a_{ij} c(j), \qquad i = 1, 2, \ldots, N.$$

Note the important point that the experimental techniques are to be coordinated with the numerical techniques. This is significant in connection with the design of experiments.

25. THE ABEL INTEGRAL EQUATION

In this concluding section, we wish to discuss the famous integral equation

(25.1) $$v(t) = \int_0^t (t - t_1)^{a-1} u(t_1)\, dt_1,$$

where $0 < a < 1$. This equation is of interest not only because it was first considered by Abel, who derived the elegant explicit solution to be found below, but also because it arises in an amazing number of contexts.

There are several approaches that may be followed. From our present standpoint, the most direct use the Laplace transform. We have

(25.2) $$L(v) = L(t^{a-1}) L(u).$$

Using the fact that

$$(25.3) \quad L(t^{a-1}) = \int_0^\infty e^{-st} t^{a-1} \, dt = \frac{1}{s^a} \int_0^\infty e^{-t} t^{a-1} \, dt = \frac{\Gamma(a)}{s^a},$$

where $\Gamma(a)$ is the Gamma function of Euler, we obtain

$$(25.4) \quad L(u) = \frac{s^a L(v)}{\Gamma(a)}.$$

We would like to use the convolution theorem to express u in terms of v. Unfortunately, s^a for $a > 0$ is not a Laplace transform. To circumvent this difficulty, we write

$$(25.5) \quad \frac{L(u)}{s} = \frac{s^{a-1} L(v)}{\Gamma(a)}.$$

Since $0 < a < 1$, s^{a-1} is a Laplace transform, namely,

$$(25.6) \quad s^{a-1} = \frac{1}{\Gamma(1-a)} \int_0^\infty e^{-st} t^{-a} \, dt.$$

Since

$$(25.7) \quad \frac{L(u)}{s} = L\left(\int_0^t u \, dt_1 \right),$$

we have from (25.5) the result

$$(25.8) \quad \int_0^t u \, dt_1 = \frac{1}{\Gamma(a)\Gamma(1-a)} \int_0^t (t - t_1)^{-a} v(t_1) \, dt_1,$$

whence Abel's result follows:

$$(25.9) \quad u(t) = \frac{1}{\Gamma(a)\Gamma(1-a)} \frac{d}{dt}\left(\int_0^t (t - t_1)^{-a} v(t_1) \, dt_1 \right).$$

We can simplify this a bit by using the classical relation

$$(25.10) \quad \Gamma(a)\Gamma(1-a) = \frac{\pi}{\sin \pi a}.$$

There is another quite interesting approach which we shall merely sketch. If n is a positive integer, the operation of integrating u n times over $[0,t]$ can be replaced by a single integral, namely,

$$(25.11) \quad \left(\int_0^t \right)^n u = \frac{1}{(n-1)!} \int_0^t (t - t_1)^{n-1} u(t_1) \, dt_1.$$

If we denote the operation $\int_0^t$ by J, we may write this

$$(25.12) \qquad J^n u = \frac{1}{(n-1)!} \int_0^t (t - t_1)^{n-1} u(t_1) \, dt_1,$$

and extend the definition of $J^n u$ to *all* $n > 0$, by writing

$$(25.13) \qquad J^n u = \frac{1}{\Gamma(n)} \int_0^t (t - t_1)^{n-1} u(t_1) \, dt_1,$$

with $\Gamma(n)$, as above, the Euler Gamma function.

It is not difficult to establish that with this definition,

$$(25.14) \qquad J^{m+n} u = J^m(J^n u),$$

for all $m,n > 0$. The Dirichlet integral used by Abel may be used to demonstrate this. Furthermore, J has an inverse, since

$$(25.15) \qquad \frac{d}{dt}\left(\int_0^t u \right) = u,$$

that is, $DJ = I$, where $D = d/dt$ and I is the identity.

It is reasonable to suspect that if we write, referring to (25.1),

$$(25.16) \qquad v = J^a[\Gamma(a)u],$$

we can, in some sense, write

$$(25.17) \qquad u = \frac{1}{\Gamma(a)} J^{-a} v.$$

However, the expression $J^{-a}v$ has not previously been defined. To do this, write

$$(25.18) \qquad u = \frac{1}{\Gamma(a)} (DJ)J^{-a}v = \frac{1}{\Gamma(a)} D(J^{1-a}v).$$

Hence,

$$(25.19) \qquad u = \frac{1}{\Gamma(a)\Gamma(1-a)} \frac{d}{dt}\left(\int_0^t (t - t_1)^{-a} v(t_1) \, dt_1 \right),$$

precisely the expression found above. References to rigorous treatments of the Abel equation will be found at the end of the chapter.

Let us turn to the numerical aspects. Suppose that $v(t)$ is given as a table of values. Without too much trouble, we can evaluate

$$\int_0^t (t - t_1)^{-a} v(t_1)\, dt_1.$$

However, the calculation of the derivative is a delicate affair which can easily introduce considerable error.

If $v(t)$ is given sufficiently accurately, the use of the Laplace transform and numerical inversion of the type applied in the previous pages yields quite satisfactory results. But what if $v(t)$ is given only to two or three significant figures, as is often the case in experimental work? Then, more sophisticated techniques are required, and this is part of the motivation of Chapter Five.

BIBLIOGRAPHY AND COMMENTS

§1.   These results were first published as a series of RAND papers in connection with a National Institutes of Health project.* See

R. BELLMAN, R. KALABA, and J. LOCKETT, *Numerical Solution of Functional Equations by Means of Laplace Transform—I: Renewal Equation*, The RAND Corporation, RM-3948-NIH, December 1963.

———, *Numerical Solution of Functional Equations by Means of Laplace Transform—II: Differential-difference Equations*, The RAND Corporation, RM-3952-NIH, December 1963.

———, *Numerical Solution of Functional Equations by Means of Laplace Transform—III: The Diffusion Equation*, The RAND Corporation, RM-3974-NIH, January 1964.

———, *Numerical Solution of Functional Equations by Means of Laplace Transform—IV: Nonlinear Equations*, The RAND Corporation, RM-4088-NIH, May 1964.

———, *Numerical Solution of Functional Equations by Means of Laplace Transform—V: Mismatched Systems of Linear Differential Equations*, The RAND Corporation, RM-4089-NIH, May 1964.

———, *Numerical Solution of Functional Equations by Means of Laplace Transform—VI: Stochastic Time-Optimal Control*, The RAND Corporation, RM-4119-PR, May 1964.

* Public Health Service Research Grant Numbers GM-09608-02 and GM-09608-03, from the Division of General Medical Sciences, National Institutes of Health.

R. BELLMAN, *Numerical Solution of Functional Equations by Means of Laplace Transform—VII: The Mellin Transform*, The RAND Corporation, RM-4179-NIH June 1964.

R. BELLMAN, R. KALABA, and J. LOCKETT, *Numerical Solution of Functional Equations by Means of Laplace Transform—VIII: Determination of Weighting Functions*, The RAND Corporation, RM-4213-NIH, September 1964.

§2.   For analytic discussions of the renewal equation, see

R. BELLMAN and K. L. COOKE, *Differential-difference Equations*, Academic Press, New York, 1963.

T. E. HARRIS, *The Theory of Branching Processes*, Springer-Verlag, Berlin, 1963.

§4.   For a brief analytic discussion of systems of renewal equations, see the book by Bellman and Cooke cited above.

§6.   The analytic aspects of these equations are treated in great detail in the previously cited book. For a different approach to the computational solution of differential-difference equations, and equations involving variable time-lags, see

R. BELLMAN and R. KALABA, *Quasilinearization and Nonlinear Boundary-value Problems*, American Elsevier, New York, 1965.
where further references will be found.

§9.   The equation $x = e^{ax}$ was studied in great detail by Ramanujan and is often referred to as Ramanujan's equation. For a detailed discussion of the roots of exponential polynomials, using the work of Pontrjagin, see the book referred to above.

§15.   For the usual approach to the numerical solution of the heat equation, see

G. E. FORSYTHE and W. WASOW, *Finite Difference Methods for Partial Differential Equations*, John Wiley & Sons, New York, 1960.
where many other references may be found.

§16.   For the solution of linear differential equations with two-point boundary conditions, see

R. BELLMAN and R. KALABA, *Quasilinearization and Nonlinear Boundary-Value Problems*, American Elsevier, New York, 1965.

§18.   Detailed discussions of the chemotherapy model will be found in

R. BELLMAN, J. JACQUEZ, and R. KALABA, "Some Mathematical Aspects of Chemotherapy—I: One-organ Models," *Bull. Math. Biophys.*, Vol. 22, 1960, pp. 181–198.
———, "The Distribution of a Drug in the Body," *Bull. Math. Biophys.*, Vol. 22, 1960, pp. 309–322.

———, "Mathematical Models of Chemotherapy," *Proc. Fourth Berkeley Symposium on Mathematical Statistics and Probability*, Vol. IV, University of California Press, Berkeley, 1961, pp. 57–66.

KOTKIN, B., *Numerical Investigations of Chemotherapy Models*, The RAND Corporation, P-2044, September 1961.

J. JACQUEZ, and B. KOTKIN, *New Version of a Two-Organ Chemotherapy Model*, The RAND Corporation, P-2154, September 1961.

B. KOTKIN, *A Mathematical Model of Drug Distribution and The Solution of Differential-difference Equations*, The RAND Corporation, RM-2907-RC, January 1962.

R. BELLMAN, J. JACQUEZ, R. KALABA, and B. KOTKIN, *A Mathematical Model of Drug Distribution in the Body: Implications for Cancer Chemotherapy*, The RAND Corporation, RM-3463-NIH, February 1963.

R. BELLMAN, and B. KOTKIN, "Differential Approximation Applied to the Solution of Convolution Equations," *Math. of Comp.*, Vol. 18, 1964, pp. 487–491.

———, *A Numerical Approach to the Convolution Equations of a Mathematical Model of Chemotherapy*, The RAND Corporation, RM-3716-NIH, July 1963.

———, *A Note on the Computational Solution of a System of Differential Equations with Varying Time Lags*, The RAND Corporation, RM-3835-NIH, November 1963.

§21. For further discussion of inverse and identification problems, see

R. BELLMAN, B. GLUSS, and R. ROTH, "Segmental Differential Approximation and the 'Black Box' Problem," *J. Math. Anal. & Appl.*, to appear.

R. BELLMAN and R. KALABA, "An Inverse Problem in Dynamic Programming and Automatic Control," *J. Math. Anal. & Appl.*, Vol. 7, 1963, pp. 322–325.

R. BELLMAN, B. GLUSS, and R. ROTH, "On the Identification of Systems and the Unscrambling of Data: Some Problems Suggested by Neurophysiology," *Proc. Nat. Acad. Sci. USA*, to appear.

R. BELLMAN, R. KALABA, and H. KAGIWADA, "Identification of Linear Systems Using Numerical Inversion of Laplace Transforms," *IEEE Trans.*, to appear.

———, "Quasilinearization, System Identification, and Prediction," *Internat. J. Engr. Sci.*, to appear.

R. BELLMAN, C. COLLIER, H. KAGIWADA, R. KALABA, and R. SELVESTER, "Estimation of Heart Parameters Using Skin Potential Measurements," *Comm. ACM*, Vol. 7, November 1964, pp. 666–668.

§22. This follows

R. BELLMAN, H. KAGIWADA, and R. KALABA, "Identification of Linear Systems Using Numerical Inversion of Laplace Transforms," *IEEE Trans.*, to appear.

§24. This problem was treated by a different technique in

J. S. BECK and A. RESCIGNO, "Determination of a Precursor Order and Particular from Kinetic Data," *J. Theoret. Biol.*, Vol. 6, 1964, pp. 1–12.

I. L. HOPKINS and R. W. HAMMING, *On Creep and Relaxation*, Bell Telephone System, Monograph 2884

E. P. C. HSIEH, *Algorithm for Solving Volterra Integral Equations Met in Process Identification*, Massachusetts Institute of Technology, Project DSR 8942, Report ESL-R-209, August 1964.

§25. See

E. T. WHITTAKER and G. N. WATSON, *Modern Analysis*, The Macmillan Co., New York, 1947.

M. TOBAK, *On Deduction of Certain Nonlinear Differential Equations from Their Solutions*, NASA Technical Note NASA TN-D-2779, Washington, D.C., 1965.

H. EDELS, K. HEARNE, and A. YOUNG, "Numerical Solutions of the Abel Integral Equation," *J. Math. Phys.*, Vol. 41, 1962, pp. 62–75,

where further references may be found.

Chapter Four

NONLINEAR EQUATIONS

I. INTRODUCTION

In Chapter Three, we considered two types of linear equations, those where $L(u)$ could be obtained in explicit fashion, and those where preliminary numerical work was required to determine it prior to an application of inversion techniques. In this chapter, all of the equations we discuss require preliminary effort, some of which may be decidedly nontrivial.

We begin with an equation which arises in the study of an idealized time-dependent neutron transport process and then continue to the discussion of the time-independent and time-dependent versions of a radiative transfer process. The reason for the prior treatment of the stationary case will be made clear in the text.

Following this, we consider an equation of novel type,

$$(1.1) \quad u_i(t) = \max_{j \neq i} \int_0^t p_{ij}(r) u_j(t - r) \, dr, \qquad i = 1, 2, \ldots, N - 1,$$

$u_N(t) = 1$, arising in an application of dynamic programming to communication networks.

Next, we wish to indicate the applicability of Laplace transform techniques to more general types of functional equations, nonlinear equations, equations with variable coefficients, and equations with variable time lags. To begin with, we shall consider the case where there are "small" deviations from linearity, where the term "smallness" will be made precise in each example.

Two types of approximation techniques will be considered, the usual method of successive approximations, and a more powerful variant based upon the theory of quasilinearization. This last approach provides part of the motivation for the methods presented in

Chapter Five for solving ill-conditioned systems of linear equations using various combinations of control theory, dynamic programming, and sequential computation.

2. A TIME-DEPENDENT NEUTRON TRANSPORT PROCESS

Consider a rod of fissionable material extending from 0 to x. A trigger neutron is introduced into the right end at time 0. In passing through a section of length Δ there is probability $a\Delta + o(\Delta)$ that an interaction takes place. The result of an interaction is that the original neutron is lost from the process, and two daughter neutrons of identical nature, one going in each direction, appear. These daughters and their progeny may also interact with the medium, but not with each other. All neutrons move with speed c. Let, under the above conditions,

(2.1) $U(x,t) = $ the expected number of neutrons emerging from the right end of the rod of length x in time t.

Then, using the familiar counting techniques of invariant imbedding, we may write

$$(2.2) \quad U\left(x + \Delta, t + \frac{2\Delta}{c}\right) = a\Delta\{1 + U(x,t)\} + (1 - a\Delta)U(x,t)$$
$$+ (1 - a\Delta)\int_0^t U_t(x,r) \, dr \, a\Delta U(x, t - r) + o(\Delta),$$

which in the limit as Δ tends to zero becomes

$$(2.3) \qquad U_x + \frac{2}{c} U_t = a + a\int_0^t U_t(x,r)U(x, t - r) \, dr.$$

The first term on the right of (2.2) is the contribution to the total number of reflected neutrons for the case in which the incident particle interacts in passing through the segment $(x, x + \Delta)$. The next two represent the contribution from processes in which the incident particle does not interact initially. The last term, $o(\Delta)$, accounts for remaining processes having probabilities proportional to a power of Δ higher than the first.

The initial conditions in space and time are readily seen to be

(2.4) $U(0,t) = 0,$ $U(x,0) = 0.$

The fact that the foregoing equation is nonlinear, that it contains partial derivatives and convolution terms, is a valid portent that there will be nontrivial difficulties in the way of any of the usual approaches to the numerical solution of partial differential equations. The convolution term, in particular, offers serious obstacles because of its significant demands on rapid-access storage. The entire past history of $U(x,r)$, $0 \leq r \leq t$, is required to advance from t to $t + \Delta$. In addition, we have the undesirable task of obtaining reliable methods of numerical solution for a novel type of functional equation. This could be a serious hindrance to the use of (2.3) as a research tool and could easily be an excellent reason for avoiding a formulation of physical processes in this manner.

To bypass these demands, we use the Laplace transform. Let

(2.5) $U_t = u(x,t),$ $L(u) = F(x,s),$

for $Re(s)$ sufficiently large, the usual assumption. The precise lower bound, as will be seen below, depends on x. Using the familiar properties of Laplace transforms with respect to derivatives and convolutions, we obtain for F the nonlinear ordinary differential equation

(2.6) $\dfrac{dF}{dx} = F^2 - 2sF + 1,$ $F(0,s) = 0.$

This Riccati equation can easily be resolved analytically, namely,

(2.7) $F(x,s) = \dfrac{\tan(x\sqrt{1 - s^2})}{\sqrt{1 - s^2} + s \tan(x\sqrt{1 - s^2})}.$

This explicit representation makes it easy via the standard inversion formula and contour shifting to obtain a quite accurate determination of the asymptotic behavior of $U(x,t)$ as $t \to \infty$, for various values of x. The leading term in the asymptotic expansion could, however, also be deduced directly from (2.6), using Tauberian techniques.

The asymptotic behavior, as we have previously emphasized, is useful both as a guide to and a check on our calculations. We have in this case, as $t \to \infty$,

(2.8) $U(x,t) \sim \tan x,$ $x < \dfrac{\pi}{2}$ (subcritical),

$U(x,t) \sim t,$ $x = \dfrac{\pi}{2}$ (critical),

$U(x,t) \sim a(x)e^{\lambda(x)t},$ $x > \dfrac{\pi}{2}$ (supercritical),

where $a(x)$ and $\lambda(x)$ are positive quantities which depend on x. The terms in parentheses are those commonly used in neutron transport theory.

3. COMPUTATIONAL RESULTS

In the figures that follow, we present some typical results of our calculations. In Figs. 4.1, 4.2, and 4.3, we expect and observe smooth curves because of the fact that the solution $U(x,t)$ approaches a finite limit as $t \to \infty$, a subcritical case.

In Fig. 4.4, we present the results of a calculation in which the shifting device was not employed. Since $U(\pi/2,t) \sim t$ as $t \to \infty$, we expect and observe some degree of numerical oscillation. In Fig. 4.5, we see the result of a calculation in which the shifting device was used, and Fig. 4.6 represents a graph obtained similarly for a supercritical case.

4. RADIATIVE TRANSFER: TIME-INDEPENDENT CASE

The application of the theory of invariant imbedding to a radiative transfer process associated with a plane-parallel slab yields the imposing, but not intransigent, equation

(4.1) $\dfrac{1}{\lambda(x)}\left[R_x + \left(\dfrac{1}{u} + \dfrac{1}{v} \right)R \right]$

$$= \left[1 + \dfrac{1}{2}\int_0^1 R(v,u',x)\,\dfrac{du'}{u'} \right]\left[1 + \dfrac{1}{2}\int_0^1 R(v',u,x)\,\dfrac{dv'}{v'} \right],$$

with the initial condition $R(v,u,0) = 0$. Here $R(v,u,x)$ represents the intensity of flux reflected from a plane-parallel slab at an angle $\cos^{-1} v$, due to flux incident at an angle $\cos^{-1} u$.

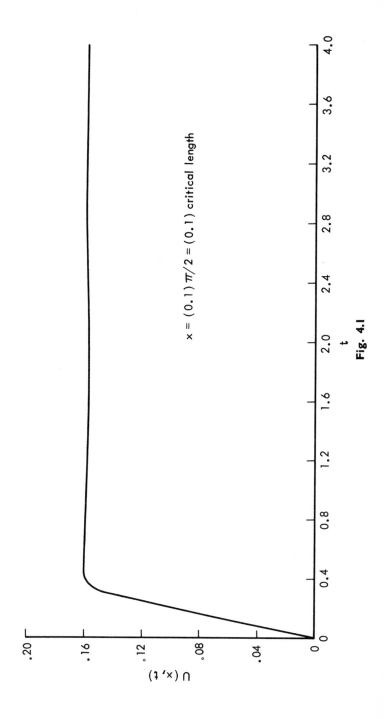

$x = (0.1)\,\pi/2 = (0.1)$ critical length

Fig. 4.1

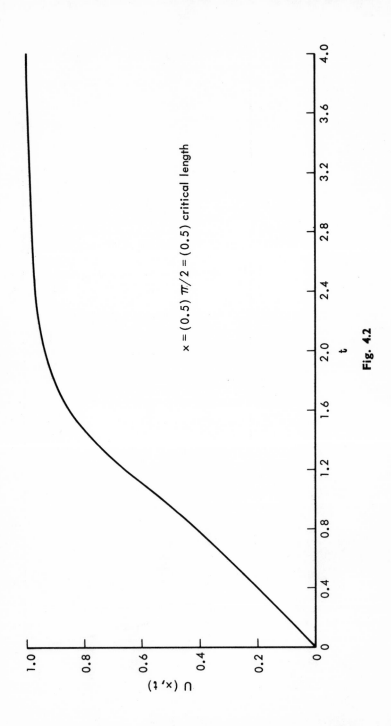

$x = (0.5) \, \pi/2 = (0.5)$ critical length

Fig. 4.2

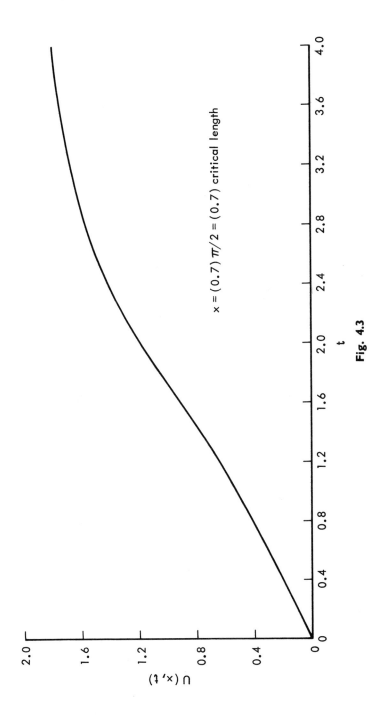

$x = (0.7)\,\pi/2 = (0.7)$ critical length

Fig. 4.3

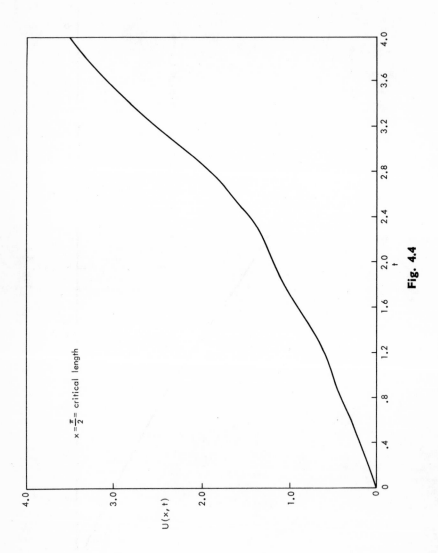

Fig. 4.4

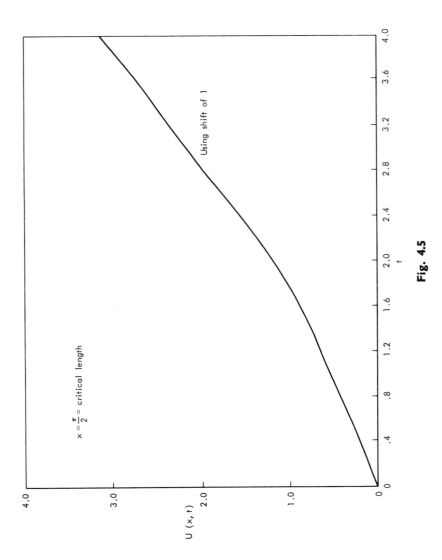

$x = \dfrac{\pi}{2} = $ critical length

Using shift of 1

U (x, t)

t

Fig. 4.5

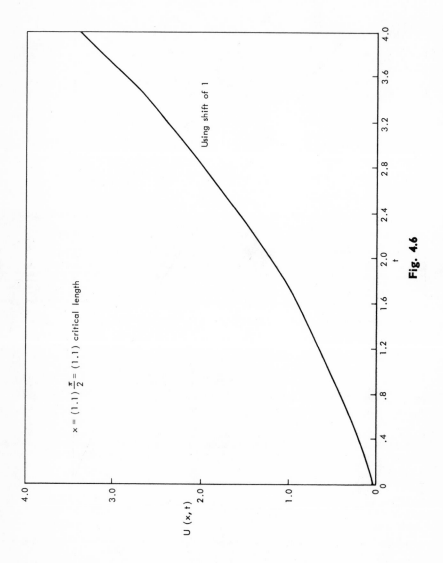

$x = (1.1)\frac{\pi}{2} = (1.1)$ critical length

Using shift of 1

U (x, t)

t

Fig. 4.6

To approach this equation computationally, we apply familiar numerical quadrature techniques and obtain the following system of ordinary differential equations

$$(4.2) \quad \frac{1}{\lambda(x)}\left[\frac{d}{dx}f_{ij}(x) + \left(\frac{1}{u_i} + \frac{1}{v_j}\right)f_{ij}(x)\right]$$

$$= \left[1 + \frac{1}{2}\sum_{k=1}^{N}\frac{w_k}{u_k}f_{ik}(x)\right]\left[1 + \frac{1}{2}\sum_{k=1}^{N}\frac{w_k}{v_k}f_{kj}(x)\right],$$

$i, j = 1, 2, \ldots, N$, with the initial conditions

$$(4.3) \qquad\qquad\qquad f_{ij}(0) = 0.$$

Here, $f_{ij}(x) = R(v_i, u_j, x)$, where v_i and u_j are the Gaussian quadrature points.

For $N = 7$ or 9, we obtain quite satisfactory results; even the values for $N = 5$ are useful for quick approximate results. In any case, with modern computers, these values of N impose no strain on rapid-access storage facilities. With some additional analytic ingenuity, we can greatly reduce these demands.

5. TIME-DEPENDENT RADIATIVE TRANSFER

Emboldened by this success, let us turn to a time-dependent version of this radiative transfer process. The problem of determining the time history of the reflected flux due to plane-parallel flux incident upon the region contained between two parallel planes leads via invariant imbedding to the rather formidable nonlinear partial differential-integral equation

$$(5.1) \quad g_x + (u^{-1} + v^{-1})(g_t + g)$$

$$= \lambda\left[\frac{H(t)}{4v} + \frac{1}{2}\int_0^1 g(v, u', x, t)\frac{du'}{u'} + \frac{1}{2v}\int_0^1 g(v', u, x, t)\, dv'\right.$$

$$\left.+ \int_0^t dt'\int_0^1 g(v', u, x, t')\, dv'\int_0^t g_t(v, u', x, t - t')\frac{du'}{u'}\right],$$

with the initial condition $g(u, v, x, 0) = 0$. Here $H(t)$ is the Heaviside unit step-function, $H(t) = 0$, $t < 0$, $H(t) = 1$, $t > 0$, and $\lambda = \lambda(x)$.

This has all of the undesirable features of the equations treated in the preceding sections, Secs. 2–4, and some additional complications of its own. Indeed, the simpler equation in the preceding section, Sec. 2, was treated first in order to give us some confidence in our techniques and some experience in this important area of time-dependent processes.

If we set

(5.2) $$P(v,u,s,x) = 4vL(g)$$

(where $L(g)$, as always, is the Laplace transform of g), we obtain the differential equation

(5.3) $P_x + (s + 1)(u^{-1} + v^{-1})P$

$$= \lambda\left\{\frac{1}{s} + \frac{1}{2}\int_0^1 P(v,u',x,s)\frac{du'}{u'} + \frac{1}{2}\int_0^1 P(v',u,x,s)\frac{dv'}{v'}\right.$$

$$\left. + \frac{s}{4}\int_0^1\int_0^1 P(v',u,x,s)P(v,u',x,s)\frac{dv'}{v'}\frac{du'}{u'}\right\},$$

with the initial condition $P(v,u,0,s) = 0$.

This equation, however, is similar in form to the equation obtained by means of invariant imbedding for the steady-state case of the foregoing problem. As in Sec. 4, it can be reduced to a system of ordinary differential equations, with initial conditions, by using quadrature formulas once again. We write

(5.4) $$\int_0^1 P(v,u',x,s)\frac{du'}{u'} = \sum_{i=1}^N \frac{w_i}{u_i}P(v,u_i,x,s),$$

$$\int_0^1 P(v',u,x,s)\frac{dv'}{v'} = \sum_{j=1}^N \frac{w_j}{v_j}P(v_j,u,x,s),$$

and then write

(5.5) $$p_{ij} = P(v_j,u_i,x,s), \qquad i,j = 1, 2, \ldots, N.$$

We see that

(5.6) $\dfrac{dp_{ij}}{dx} + (s + 1)(u_i^{-1} + v_j^{-1})p_{ij}$

$$= \lambda\left\{\frac{1}{s} + \frac{1}{2}\sum_{k=1}^N \frac{w_k}{u_k}p_{kj} + \frac{1}{2}\sum_{l=1}^N \frac{w_l}{v_l}p_{il} + \frac{s}{4}\sum_{k,l=1}^N \frac{w_k w_l}{u_k v_l}p_{il}p_{kj}\right\},$$

with the initial conditions $P_{ij}(0) = 0$, $i,j = 1, 2, \ldots, N$.

6. SOME NUMERICAL RESULTS

Some typical numerical results are shown in graphical form in Fig. 4.7. Note the monotone behavior and the approach to the correct limiting values as t increases. Earlier calculations devoted to the steady-state situations had provided these limiting values, which provide such an important check on the calculations in the transient case.

7. A DYNAMIC PROGRAMMING PROCESS

Let us consider a physical system which may be in one of N possible states numbered 1, 2, ..., N. We suppose that the time involved in transforming the system from state i to state j is a random variable with a known probability density function,

(7.1) $\displaystyle\int_0^b p_{ij}(t)\, dt =$ probability that the transformation from state i to state j is completed in time b or less.

We also assume that the times taken in making the various transformations from a given state to the desired terminal state, which we take to be the state N, are independent random variables. Our aim is to determine the sequence of transformations starting in state i which maximize the probability of arriving in state N in time t or less, $t \geq 0$. We also wish to determine the optimal policy, that is, the rule telling us what transformation is made as a function of the state i and the time t remaining. Let us introduce the functions

(7.2) $u_i(t) =$ the probability that the system is transformed from state i to the desired terminal state N in time t or less using an optimal transformation policy, $i = 1, 2, \ldots, N$ and $t \geq 0$.

In particular, let us note that

(7.3) $$u_N(t) = 1, \qquad t \geq 0.$$

Employment of the principle of optimality then yields in the usual fashion the basic system of equations

(7.4) $\displaystyle u_i(t) = \max_{j \neq i} \int_0^t p_{ij}(r) u_j(t - r)\, dr, \qquad i = 1, 2, \ldots, N - 1.$

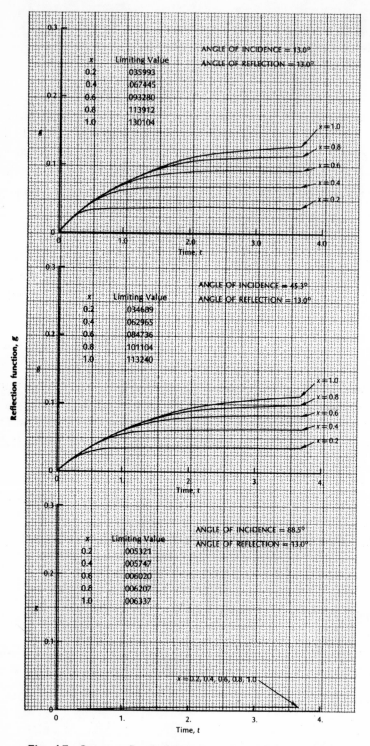

Fig. 4.7—Some reflection functions for slabs of various thicknesses, with albedo 0.7

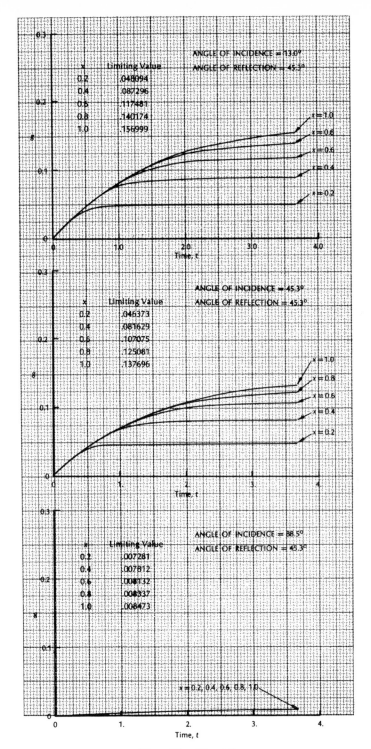

Fig. 4.7—(Cont'd)

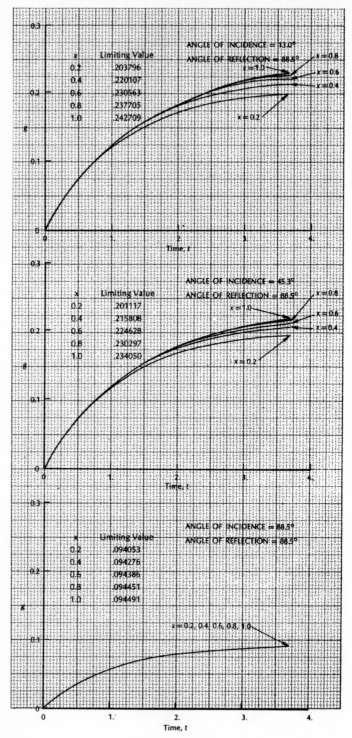

Fig. 4.7—(Cont'd)

8. NUMERICAL TREATMENT

The nonlinear functional equations in (7.4) offer certain difficulties in their numerical solution due, in part, to the appearance of the convolution integrals. Notice that the numerical production of the value of the integral $\int_0^t p_{ij}(r)u_j(t-r)\,dr$ involves storing the function u_j on the entire interval $(0,t)$. This can effectively block solution if N is large due to the limited number of rapid-access storage cells in current computing devices. Use of the Laplace transform combined with a numerical inversion scheme offers certain attractive features, especially since the functions $u_i(t)$ are monotone bounded functions of t, which we expect to be quite smooth—assuming, of course, as we shall, that the $p_{ij}(t)$ are smooth functions.

We employ Picard's method of successive approximations

$$(8.1) \quad \begin{cases} u_i^{(k+1)}(t) = \max_{j \neq i} \int_0^t p_{ij}(t)u_j^{(k)}(t-r)\,dr, \\ \qquad\qquad\qquad\qquad\qquad i = 1, 2, \ldots, N-1, \quad k = 0, \ldots; \\ u_N(t) = 1, \end{cases}$$

to solve (7.4). In this case, the function $u_i^{(k)}(t)$ has a simple physical interpretation. Next, we introduce the Laplace transforms

$$(8.2) \quad L\{u_i^{(k)}(t)\} = U_i^{(k)}(s), \qquad i = 1, 2, \ldots, N, k = 1, 2, \ldots,$$

$$(8.3) \quad L\{p_{ij}(t)\} = P_{ij}(s), \qquad i = 1, 2, \ldots, N,$$
$$j = 1, 2, \ldots, i-1, i+1, \ldots, N.$$

To calculate the right-hand side of (8.1), we multiply the Laplace transforms of the functions $p_{ij}(t)$ and $u_j^{(k)}(t)$, invert the resulting transform numerically, and for each of the finite sets of values of t, maximize over the index j. This maximization is carried out by means of a direct search procedure. As an initial approximation we may use the equations

$$(8.4) \quad u_i^{(0)}(t) = \begin{cases} 0, & i \neq N, \\ 1, & i = N. \end{cases}$$

Much better initial approximations can be obtained in a number of ways.

9. A NUMERICAL EXAMPLE

Consider the directed graph shown in Fig. 4.8. We assume that the probability density functions for the random times of transition are of the form

$$(9.1) \qquad p_{ij}(t) = \begin{cases} 0, & t < t_{ij} - a_{ij}, \\ \dfrac{1}{2a_{ij}}, & t_{ij} - a_{ij} \le t \le t_{ij} + a_{ij}, \\ 0, & t > t_{ij} + a_{ij}, \end{cases}$$

and that only the transitions shown are allowable. The values of the parameters t_{ij} and a_{ij} are as shown in the figure.

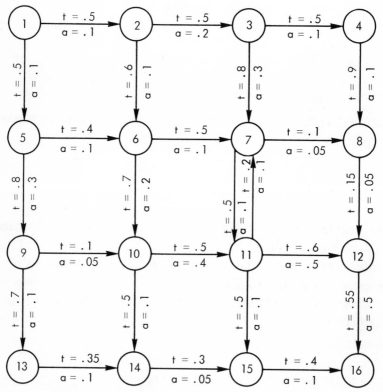

Fig. 4.8—The graph of allowable transformations

A numerical experiment was conducted using the method described above to determine the optimal decisions and probabilities. The probabilities are the functions $u_i(t)$, which are solutions of (7.4), and the optimal decisions are the functions $j_i(t)$, which represent the maximizing values of j at each state i for each time remaining t. Physically, they represent the correct choice of the next state, the system currently being in state i and time t remaining. The calculation was done in double precision and consumed about one minute of running time on the IBM-7090, with no attempt having been made to streamline the calculation. Ten stages in the Picard successive approximation scheme were carried out, although no changes occurred after the sixth iteration, and a ten-point quadrature formula was used. Use of a seven-point formula gave results in good agreement.

The results of the tenth iteration are reproduced on the following pages.

The calculated probabilities of transforming the system from state i to state N in time t or less are not completely accurate, as evidenced by the appearance of probabilities greater than one, but they do follow the correct trend. The probabilities are monotone increasing as t increases. The numerical inaccuracies are caused by round-off errors, errors in the determination of the Laplace transforms, and the ill-conditioned nature of the linear systems to be solved.* The probabilities seem to be accurate, however, to two decimal figures. In any case, these results can be used as a basis for a quick judgement concerning the effectiveness of a communication network, as the basis for a more refined numerical scheme based upon different principles, or as motivation for using more accurate numerical techniques of the same type.

10. NONLINEAR DIFFERENTIAL EQUATIONS

Let us now turn our attention to some nonlinear differential equations of conventional type. Our aim is to show that a combination

---

* The numerical inversion in this case was done using a routine for the solution of linear systems of algebraic equations.

APPROXIMATION NO. 10

STATION	TIME		PROBABILITY I TO N		NEXT STATION
1	0.43392172	01	0.10827479	01	2
	0.26960971	01	0.89716081	00	5
	0.18307380	01	0.16419911	-00	5
	0.12612407	01	0.14228301	-01	2
	0.85434268	00	0.77359194	-02	5
	0.55436455	00	0.66359219	-02	2
	0.33310115	-00	0.15076907	-02	5
	0.17470489	-00	0.35050916	-02	2
	0.69852151	-01	0.68542773	-03	5
	0.13132592	-01	0.16912048	-02	2

STATION	TIME		PROBABILITY I TO N		NEXT STATION
2	0.43392172	01	0.10356133	01	6
	0.26960971	01	0.10338742	01	6
	0.18307380	01	0.43726414	-00	6
	0.12612407	01	0.91872898	-03	6
	0.85434268	00	0.16393144	-01	6
	0.55436455	00	0.		6
	0.33310115	-00	0.52366558	-02	6
	0.17470489	-00	0.		6
	0.69852151	-01	0.28805911	-02	6
	0.13132592	-01	0.		6

STATION	TIME		PROBABILITY I TO N		NEXT STATION
3	0.43392172	01	0.10162964	01	7
	0.26960971	01	0.10328768	01	7
	0.18307380	01	0.73211797	00	7
	0.12612407	01	0.17594333	-00	7
	0.85434268	00	0.12417017	-01	4
	0.55436455	00	0.		7
	0.33310115	-00	0.54102473	-02	4
	0.17470489	-00	0.		7
	0.69852151	-01	0.28573324	-02	4
	0.13132592	-01	0.		7

STATION	TIME		PROBABILITY I TO N		NEXT STATION
4	0.43392172	01	0.99046067	00	8
	0.26960971	01	0.10219196	01	8
	0.18307380	01	0.75002653	00	8
	0.12612407	01	0.14808361	-00	8
	0.85434268	00	-0.		8
	0.55436455	00	0.85749871	-03	8
	0.33310115	-00	0.17485913	-03	8
	0.17470489	-00	0.		8
	0.69852151	-01	0.42152344	-03	8
	0.13132592	-01	0.		8

STATION	TIME		PROBABILITY I TO N		NEXT STATION
5	0.43392172	01	0.10477711	01	9
	0.26960971	01	0.10678057	01	6
	0.18307380	01	0.64533605	00	6
	0.12612407	01	0.83425282	-01	6
	0.85434268	00	0.19007171	-01	9
	0.55436455	00	0.40503145	-02	6
	0.33310115	-00	0.44332147	-02	9
	0.17470489	-00	0.		9
	0.69852151	-01	0.23066492	-02	9
	0.13132592	-01	0.		9

STATION	TIME		PROBABILITY I TO N		NEXT STATION
6	0.43392172	01	0.10218611	01	7
	0.26960971	01	0.10769513	01	10
	0.18307380	01	0.94570085	00	7
	0.12612407	01	0.46827190	-00	7
	0.85434268	00	0.72981026	-01	7
	0.55436455	00	0.		10
	0.33310115	-00	0.12560558	-01	10
	0.17470489	-00	0.		10
	0.69852151	-01	0.68500499	-02	10
	0.13132592	-01	0.		10

STATION	TIME		PROBABILITY I TO N		NEXT STATION
7	0.43392172	01	0.10267277	01	11
	0.26960971	01	0.10190086	01	11
	0.18307380	01	0.10263501	01	11
	0.12612407	01	0.92956052	00	8
	0.85434268	00	0.55565539	00	8
	0.55436455	00	0.25432004	-00	8
	0.33310115	-00	0.42225652	-01	8
	0.17470489	-00	0.65395803	-02	11
	0.69852151	-01	0.13714995	-02	8
	0.13132592	-01	0.29403214	-02	11

STATION	TIME		PROBABILITY I TO N		NEXT STATION
8	0.43392172	01	0.99956034	00	12
	0.26960971	01	0.10004416	01	12
	0.18307380	01	0.10008449	01	12
	0.12612407	01	0.97845254	00	12
	0.85434268	00	0.66315357	00	12
	0.55436455	00	0.35186177	-00	12
	0.33310115	-00	0.13215611	-00	12
	0.17470489	-00	0.41543778	-02	12
	0.69852151	-01	0.14964093	-02	12
	0.13132592	-01	0.		12

STATION	TIME		PROBABILITY I TO N		NEXT STATION
9	0.43392172	01	0.10228847	01	10
	0.26960971	01	0.10709345	01	13
	0.18307380	01	0.10498347	01	10
	0.12612407	01	0.46587164	-00	10
	0.85434268	00	0.36640662	-01	13
	0.55436455	00	0.34709365	-01	10
	0.33310115	-00	0.17275571	-01	13
	0.17470489	-00	0.15240405	-01	10
	0.69852151	-01	0.94038325	-02	13
	0.13132592	-01	0.41870604	-02	10

STATION	TIME		PROBABILITY I TO N		NEXT STATION
10	0.43392172	01	0.10217889	01	11
	0.26960971	01	0.10307600	01	11
	0.18307380	01	0.10680886	01	14
	0.12612407	01	0.62766343	00	14
	0.85434268	00	0.49920902	-01	11
	0.55436455	00	0.34847025	-01	14
	0.33310115	-00	-0.		14
	0.17470489	-00	0.16278479	-01	14
	0.69852151	-01	-0.		14
	0.13132592	-01	0.72924925	-02	14

STATION	TIME		PROBABILITY I TO N		NEXT STATION
11	0.43392172	01	0.10287464	01	7
	0.26960971	01	0.10198842	01	15
	0.18307380	01	0.10256068	01	7
	0.12612407	01	0.10515503	01	15
	0.85434268	00	0.38860332	-00	15
	0.55436455	00	0.83176410	-01	12
	0.33310115	-00	0.33980217	-01	15
	0.17470489	-00	0.53636457	-02	7
	0.69852151	-01	0.15008017	-01	15
	0.13132592	-01	0.19082632	-02	7

STATION	TIME		PROBABILITY I TO N		NEXT STATION
12	0.43392172	01	0.99755352	00	16
	0.26960971	01	0.10041457	01	16
	0.18307380	01	0.99338845	00	16
	0.12612407	01	0.10112759	01	16
	0.85434268	00	0.81845825	00	16
	0.55436455	00	0.49707697	-00	16
	0.33310115	-00	0.28758071	-00	16
	0.17470489	-00	0.12170310	-00	16
	0.69852151	-01	0.22935487	-01	16
	0.13132592	-01	-0.35441821	-02	16

STATION	TIME		PROBABILITY I TO N		NEXT STATION
13	0.43392172	01	0.10038669	01	14
	0.26960971	01	0.99232167	00	14
	0.18307380	01	0.10179383	01	14
	0.12612407	01	0.89907813	00	14
	0.85434268	00	0.87549866	-01	14
	0.55436455	00	0.		14
	0.33310115	-00	0.35995010	-02	14
	0.17470489	-00	0.		14
	0.69852151	-01	0.79478162	-03	14
	0.13132592	-01	0.		14

STATION	TIME		PROBABILITY I TO N		NEXT STATION
14	0.43392172	01	0.99766014	00	15
	0.26960971	01	0.10042068	01	15
	0.18307380	01	0.99239152	00	15
	0.12612407	01	0.10177900	01	15
	0.85434268	00	0.89782470	00	15
	0.55436455	00	0.82336294	-01	15
	0.33310115	-00	-0.		15
	0.17470489	-00	0.41829141	-02	15
	0.69852151	-01	-0.		15
	0.13132592	-01	0.10027616	-02	15

STATION	TIME		PROBABILITY I TO N		NEXT STATION
15	0.43392172	01	0.99739495	00	16
	0.26960971	01	0.10040696	01	16
	0.18307380	01	0.99457508	00	16
	0.12612407	01	0.10067742	01	16
	0.85434268	00	0.99313949	00	16
	0.55436455	00	0.97760368	00	16
	0.33310115	-00	0.22744811	-00	16
	0.17470489	-00	-0.38564794	-01	16
	0.69852151	-01	0.18773596	-01	16
	0.13132592	-01	-0.10102269	-01	16

STATION	TIME		PROBABILITY I TO N		NEXT STATION
16	0.43392172	01	0.09999999	01	16
	0.26960971	01	0.09999999	01	16
	0.18307380	01	0.09999999	01	16
	0.12612407	01	0.09999999	01	16
	0.85434268	00	0.09999999	01	16
	0.55436455	00	0.09999999	01	16
	0.33310115	-00	0.09999999	01	16
	0.17470489	-00	0.09999999	01	16
	0.69852151	-01	0.09999999	01	16
	0.13132592	-01	0.09999999	01	16

of the Laplace transform and various methods of successive approximations yields feasible techniques for obtaining numerical solutions. Let us begin with the simple differential equation

(10.1) $$u' = -u - u^2, \qquad u(0) = c.$$

where c is taken to be nonnegative and, at this stage of the game, small, for example; c is of the order of magnitude of 0.1 or 0.5. That the equation possesses a simple explicit solution is of no matter to us. Taking Laplace transforms, we have

(10.2) $$L(u') = -L(u) - L(u^2),$$

or, in the usual fashion,

(10.3) $$L(u) = \frac{c - L(u^2)}{(s + 1)}.$$

We will solve this nonlinear integral equation numerically by way of successive approximations combined with numerical quadrature. Let $u_0(t)$ be the solution of

(10.4) $$L(u_0) = \frac{c}{s + 1}.$$

In this case, we see that $u_0 = ce^{-t}$, but this explicit analytic representation is of no importance to us here since we are interested in general procedures. We employ the foregoing quadrature techniques to obtain the values $\{u_0(t_i)\}$, $i = 1, 2, \ldots, N$.

Next, we determine u_1 by means of the equation

(10.5) $$L(u_1) = \frac{c - L(u_0^2)}{s + 1}.$$

To evaluate the expression $L(u_0^2)$, we employ the same quadrature formula

(10.6) $$L(u_0^2) = \sum_{i=1}^{N} w_i u_0^2(t_i) r_i^{s-1}.$$

Since the quantities $u_0^2(t_i)$ have already been determined, we can employ our inversion methods to determine $\{u_1(t_i)\}$, $i = 1, 2, \ldots, N$.

Continuing in this way, we determine the values $\{u_n(t_i)\}$ by means of the relation

(10.7) $$L(u_n) = \frac{c - L(u_{n-1}^2)}{(s + 1)}.$$

Naturally, we expect that this procedure will converge only for $|c|$ sufficiently small. We shall discuss this point again below.

II. NUMERICAL RESULTS

In Figs. 4.9 and 4.10, we compare the results of direct numerical integration of the differential equation with the integration technique described above.

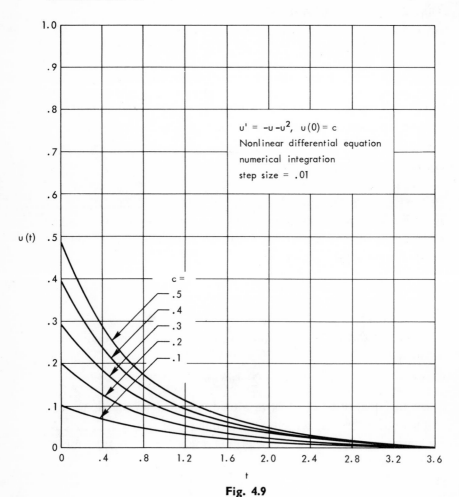

$u' = -u - u^2, \quad u(0) = c$
Nonlinear differential equation
numerical integration
step size $= .01$

$c =$
.5
.4
.3
.2
.1

Fig. 4.9

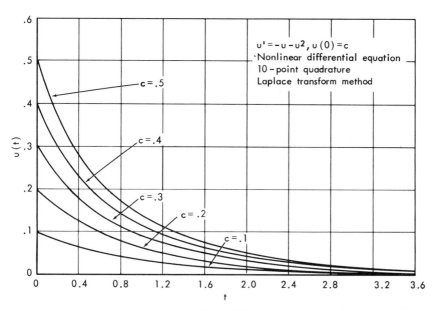

Fig. 4.10

12. ALTERNATE APPROACH

Returning to (10.3), we see that quadrature applied simultaneously to both terms, $L(u)$ and $L(u^2)$, yields the system of simultaneous nonlinear algebraic equations

$$(12.1) \qquad \sum_{i=1}^{N} w_i u(t_i) r_i^{s-1} = \frac{c - \sum_{i=1}^{N} w_i u^2(t_i) r_i^{s-1}}{s + 1},$$

for $s = 1, 2, \ldots, N$.

In the previous sections, we solved these equations by means of successive approximations. Let us consider some alternative approaches. Let

$$(12.2) \qquad v_1 = \begin{pmatrix} u(t_1) \\ u(t_2) \\ \cdot \\ \cdot \\ \cdot \\ u(t_n) \end{pmatrix}, \qquad v_2 = \begin{pmatrix} u^2(t_1) \\ u^2(t_2) \\ \cdot \\ \cdot \\ \cdot \\ u^2(t_n) \end{pmatrix}$$

and D denote the diagonal matrix

$$(12.3) \qquad D = \begin{pmatrix} \frac{1}{2} & & & & 0 \\ & \frac{1}{3} & & & \\ & & \ddots & & \\ 0 & & & & \frac{1}{N+1} \end{pmatrix},$$

and $A = (w_i r_i^{s-1})$, $i, s = 1, 2, \ldots, N$. Then (12.1) may be written

$$(12.4) \qquad\qquad Av_1 = Dc - DAv_2.$$

Thus

$$(12.5) \qquad\qquad v_1 = A^{-1}Dc - A^{-1}DAv_2.$$

Since A^{-1} is known numerically to as many significant figures as desired, we can obtain $A^{-1}Dc$ and $A^{-1}DA$ as accurately as we wish.

It follows that we finally obtain a system of nonlinear equations of the form

$$(12.6) \qquad u(t_i) = b_i + \sum_{j=1}^{N} c_{ij} u^2(t_j), \qquad i = 1, 2, \ldots, N,$$

where the c_{ij} are known numerical values.

These equations can be solved by means of iteration, as indicated above, that is,

$$(12.7) \qquad u_n(t_i) = b_i + \sum_{j=1}^{N} c_{ij} u_{n-1}^2(t_j), \qquad i = 1, 2, \ldots, N,$$

or by use of the multidimensional Lagrange expansion formula or by means of more sophisticated techniques of successive approximations such as the Newton-Raphson technique in multidimensional form.

Observe that the quantities b_i and c_{ij} are independent of the analytic form of the nonlinear term. Thus, if the equation were

$$(12.8) \qquad u' = -u + g(u), \qquad u(0) = c,$$

the form of (12.7) would be

$$(12.9) \qquad\qquad u(t_i) = b_i + \sum_{j=1}^{N} c_{ij} g[u(t_j)].$$

In most cases, the method is not significant as far as ordinary differential equations are concerned, because of the availability of powerful standard methods for numerical solution. It may, however, be of use in the study of nonlinear mismatched systems.

13. A DIFFERENTIAL-DIFFERENCE EQUATION

When we come to functional equations of a more complicated nature, the method described above begins to assume great significance. Consider, for example, the nonlinear differential-difference equation

$$(13.1) \quad u'(t) = -u(t-1) - u^2(t), \qquad u(t) = c, \qquad -1 \le t \le 0.$$

We have

$$(13.2) \qquad L(u)(s + e^s) = c - \int_0^1 ce^{-st}\,dt - L(u^2).$$

Hence, following the procedure used above, we compute $u_0(t)$ by means of the relation

$$(13.3) \qquad L(u_0) = \frac{c - \int_0^1 ce^{-st}\,dt}{s + e^{-s}},$$

and then u_1 from the relation

$$(13.4) \qquad L(u_1) = \frac{c - \int_0^1 ce^{-st}\,dt - L(u_0^2)}{(s + e^{-s})},$$

and so on.

The important point to note is that despite the great increase in complexity of a differential-difference equation over an ordinary differential equation, the computational time and effort required is virtually the same. Once again, we have convergence only if $|c|$ is sufficiently small.

14. NUMERICAL RESULTS

In Fig. 4.11, we indicate the use of different numbers of quadrature points. Observe, as before, that the accuracy of the solution fails for large t.

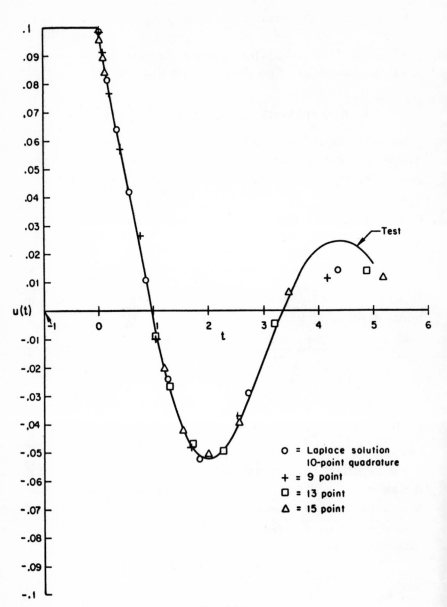

Fig. 4.11

15. A HEAT EQUATION

Consider next the nonlinear heat equation

(15.1) $$k(x)u_t = u_{xx} + bg(u),$$
$$u(0,t) = u(1,t) = 0,$$
$$u(x,0) = h(x).$$

Using the Laplace transform, we readily obtain the ordinary differential equation

(15.2) $$L(u)'' - sk(x)L(u) = -k(x)h(x) - bL(g(u)),$$

with the two-point boundary condition

(15.3) $$L(u) = 0, \qquad x = 0, 1.$$

Here $'$ denotes d/dx.

As above, we employ successive approximations. Let u_0 be the solution of

(15.4) $$L(u_0)'' - sk(x)L(u_0) = -k(x)h(x),$$
$$L(u_0) = 0, \qquad x = 0, 1.$$

First we solve the differential equation numerically for a set of s-values, $s = 1, 2, \ldots, N$, and then we use the Laplace inversion technique. Storing the values $\{u_0(x,t_i)\}$ for $x = 0, \Delta, 2\Delta, \ldots, M\Delta = 1$, we then solve the equation

(15.5) $$L(u_1)'' - sk(x)L(u_1) = -k(x)h(x) - bL(g(u_0)),$$
$$L(u_1) = 0, \qquad x = 0, 1.$$

Continuing in this way, we obtain a sequence of functions $\{u_n(x,t_i)\}$, evaluated at the foregoing x-values.

16. NUMERICAL RESULTS

To illustrate the technique, we considered the equation

(16.1) $$4u_t = u_{xx} + \frac{u^2}{10}, \qquad u(x,0) = \sin \pi x,$$
$$u(0,t) = u(1,t) = 0.$$

(See Fig. 4.12).

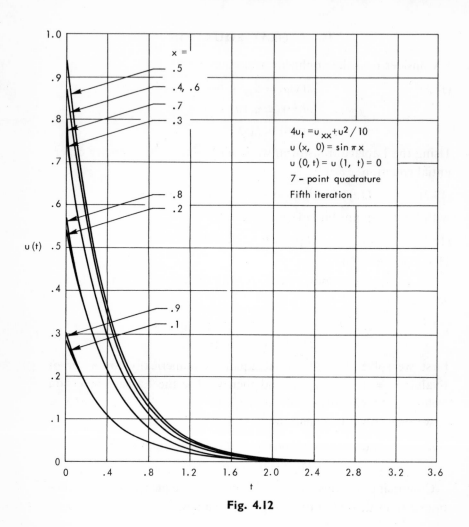

Fig. 4.12

17. PERTURBATION TECHNIQUES

Let us now discuss another technique, a perturbation method. Returning to the equation

(17.1) $u' = -u - u^2, \qquad u(0) = c,$

let us think of the nonlinear term as representing a "small" effect, and indicate this by writing

(17.2) $\qquad\qquad u' = -u - \epsilon u^2, \qquad u(0) = c,$

where ϵ is a parameter introduced for our convenience. Let us now look for a solution of (17.2) of the form

(17.3) $\qquad\qquad u = u_0 + \epsilon u_1 + \epsilon^2 u_2 + \cdots,$

where the u_i are functions of t. Substituting in (17.2), we obtain the relation

(17.4) $\qquad \displaystyle\sum_{n=0}^{\infty} \epsilon^n u'_n = -\sum_{n=0}^{\infty} \epsilon^n u_n - \epsilon \sum_{n=0}^{\infty} \left(\sum_{k=0}^{n} u_k u_{n-k} \right) \epsilon^n.$

Equating coefficients of ϵ, we obtain the system of equations

(17.5) $\qquad u'_0 = -u_0, \qquad\qquad\qquad u_0(0) = c,$

$\qquad\qquad\quad u'_1 = -u_1 - u_0^2, \qquad\qquad u_1(0) = 0,$

$\qquad\qquad\quad \vdots$

$\qquad\qquad\quad u'_n = -u_n - \displaystyle\sum_{k=0}^{n-1} u_k u_{n-1-k}, \qquad u_n(0) = 0.$

The n-th equation is linear in u_n. Solving these recurrently, via the Laplace transform, we have

(17.6) $\qquad\qquad L(u_n) = \dfrac{-\displaystyle\sum_{k=0}^{n-1} L(u_k u_{n-1-k})}{(s + 1)}.$

We now employ the inversion formula in the usual fashion to determine $u_0, u_1, \ldots$, recurrently, or simultaneously. Then, $u(t)$ is obtained via (17.3).

18. CONVERGENCE ASPECTS

Let us now examine the question of convergence of the series in (17.3). The exact solution of (17.2), with $c = 1$, is given by

(18.1) $\qquad\qquad u = \dfrac{e^{-t}}{1 + \epsilon(1 - e^{-t})}.$

This is readily obtained by straightforward separation of variables in (17.2). It is clear that the power series solution of u in terms of ϵ,

$$(18.2) \qquad u = e^{-t} - \epsilon(1 - e^{-t}) + \epsilon^2(1 - e^{-t})^2 - \cdots,$$

is convergent only if $|1 - e^{-t}| < 1$. Yet the solution in (18.1) is a well-behaved function for *all* $\epsilon \geq 0$. The barrier to convergence of (18.2) for all positive ϵ is due to the singularity at a negiatve value of ϵ, $\epsilon = -(1 - e^{-t})^{-1}$.

What can we do about this? Suppose that we set

$$(18.3) \qquad \frac{\epsilon}{1 + \epsilon} = \lambda, \quad \text{or} \quad \epsilon = \frac{\lambda}{1 - \lambda}.$$

We see that $0 \leq \lambda \leq 1$ for all $\epsilon \geq 0$. Then

$$(18.4) \qquad u = \frac{e^{-t}}{1 + \dfrac{\lambda(1 - e^{-t})}{1 - \lambda}} = \frac{(1 - \lambda)e^{-t}}{1 - \lambda e^{-t}}.$$

It follows that u can be expressed as a power series in λ for $|\lambda| < 1$, which means for all positive ϵ. To obtain this series, we return to (17.2), and write

$$(18.5) \qquad u' = -u - \frac{\lambda}{1 - \lambda} u^2, \qquad u(0) = 1,$$

$$u = w_0 + \lambda w_1 + \lambda^2 w_2 + \cdots.$$

Proceeding as before, we determine the coefficient functions, the w_i recurrently. When we are through, we have an expansion of the form

$$(18.6) \qquad u = w_0 + \frac{\epsilon}{1 + \epsilon} w_1 + \left(\frac{\epsilon}{1 + \epsilon}\right)^2 w_2 + \cdots,$$

valid for *all* $\epsilon \geq 0$.

19. DISCUSSION

What we have performed, in complex variable terms, is a mapping of the interval of interest $\epsilon \geq 0$ into an interval $0 \leq \lambda \leq 1$. How did we know what to do? In this case, we used our knowledge of the behavior of u as a function of the complex variable ϵ. In general, this is a very difficult question to answer. Without the aid of an explicit solution, we usually indulge in some mathematical experimentation and see what happens. With modern computers, this experimental approach is feasible.

The perturbation method must always be used with great care, since the properties of the solutions of nonlinear equations do not necessarily depend in a continuous fashion on the values of the parameters. Examples of this are given in the references at the end of this chapter.

20. LINEAR EQUATIONS WITH VARIABLE COEFFICIENTS

There is no difficulty in extending the previous methods to the case where both nonlinearities and variable coefficients appear. For example, if the heat equation of Sec. 1 had the form

$$(20.1) \qquad k(x)u_t = u_{xx} + g(t)u,$$

with the same initial and boundary conditions, we would write

$$(20.2) \qquad L(u_{n+1})'' - sk(x)L(u_{n+1}) = -k(x)h(x) - L(g(t)u_n),$$

and proceed as before.

We can also apply perturbation techniques upon writing $\epsilon g(t)u$, and so on.

Let us also note in passing that equations of the form

$$(20.3) \qquad u'(t) = au(t) + bu(t - \phi(t)), \qquad u(0) = c,$$

may also be treated by means of a combination of the Laplace transform and successive approximations. We suppose that $\phi(0) = 0$, $t \geq \phi(t) \geq 0$, and that $t - \phi(t) = t_1$ has a unique solution $t = h(t_1)$. Then, in a familiar fashion,

$$(20.4) \qquad L(u) = \frac{c}{s - a} + \frac{bL[u(t - \phi(t))]}{s - a}.$$

Now

(20.5)
$$L[u(t - \phi(t))] = \int_0^\infty u(t - \phi(t))e^{-st}\, dt$$

$$= \int_0^\infty h'(t_1)u(t_1)e^{-sh(t_1)}\, dt_1.$$

We may now use quadrature techniques and successive approximations as before.

21. QUASILINEARIZATION

The usual, and valid, objection to the straightforward Picard iteration technique employed in the previous sections, is that the rate of convergence is generally slow. This means that the error introduced by the numerical solution can be considerable. In the situations where it does converge, we commonly possess an estimate of the form

(21.1)
$$|u_n - u| \le a_1 r^n,$$

where $r < 1$.

We can obtain much more rapid convergence by using quasi-linearization techniques (which in some cases is equivalent to the algorithm provided by the Newton-Raphson-Kantorovich method). Thus, for example, instead of using the recurrence relation

(21.2)
$$u'_{n+1} = u_{n+1} - g(u_n), \qquad u_{n+1}(0) = c,$$

we use

(21.3)
$$u'_{n+1} = -u_{n+1} - g(u_n) - (u_{n+1} - u_n)g'(u_n),$$

$$u_{n+1}(0) = c.$$

The right-hand side is the expansion of $-(u + g(u))$ about the point $u = u_n$, up to *quadratic* terms. It is now easy to show that

(21.4)
$$|u_n - u| \le a_1 r^{2^n},$$

or, alternatively, that

(21.5)
$$|u_{n+1} - u_n| \le b_1 |u_n - u_{n-1}|^2, \qquad b_1 < 1,$$

for $0 \le t \le t_0$.

The disadvantage of this approach, as far as the use of the Laplace transform is concerned, lies in the fact that u_{n+1} satisfies a linear equation with *variable* coefficients. Thus, we obtain

(21.6) $sL(u_{n+1}) - c = -L(u_{n+1}) - L(u_{n+1}g'(u_n)) - L(g(u_n) - u_ng'(u_n))$

We can use quadrature techniques, as before, to evaluate $L(u_{n+1}g'(u_n))$, *but* we now have a different matrix of coefficients for the unknown quantities $\{u_{n+1}(t_i)\}$ at each stage. We no longer possess the luxury of an explicit tabulated inverse. Furthermore, this matrix is ill-conditioned, to a minor or major extent.

All of this leads to a consideration of how to solve ill-conditioned systems of linear equations—if we have no other recourse. This will be the subject of the next chapter, where additional motivation for this study is provided.

BIBLIOGRAPHY AND COMMENTS

§1. The area of nonlinear functional equations is a jungle in which pitfalls, morasses, and traps for the unwary and inexperienced abound. Very little is known analytically, and computationally the situation is even starker.

For an elementary introduction to the methods we describe here, see

R. BELLMAN, *Perturbation Techniques in Mathematics, Physics, and Engineering*, Holt, Rinehart & Winston, New York, 1964.
where many other references will be found.

§2. These results were first presented in

R. BELLMAN, R. KALABA, and M. PRESTRUD, "On the New Computational Solution of Time-dependent Transport Processes—I: One-dimensional Case," *Proc. Nat. Acad. Sci. USA*, Vol. 47, 1961, pp. 1072–1074.
See also
R. BELLMAN, H. KAGIWADA, R. KALABA, and M. PRESTRUD, *Invariant Imbedding and Time-Dependent Processes*, American Elsevier, New York, 1964.

§4. See

R. BELLMAN, R. KALABA, and M. PRESTRUD, *Invariant Imbedding and Radiative Transfer in Slabs of Finite Thickness*, American Elsevier, New York, 1963, for a detailed account.

§5. See

R. BELLMAN, H. KAGIWADA, R. KALABA, and M. PRESTRUD, *Invariant Imbedding and Time-Dependent Processes*, American Elsevier, New York, 1964.

§7. For an introduction to dynamic programming and routing problems, see

R. BELLMAN, and S. DREYFUS, *Applied Dynamic Programming*, Princeton University Press, Princeton, New Jersey, 1962.

R. KALABA, "On Some Communication Network Problems," *Combinatorial Analysis*, R. Bellman and M. Hall, eds., American Mathematical Society Providence, Rhode Island, 1960.

§10. For detailed discussion and further references, see

R. BELLMAN, *Stability Theory of Differential Equations*, McGraw-Hill, New York, 1953.

§12. See the book cited in the bibliography for Sec. 1 for a discussion of the one-dimensional Lagrange expansion formula and references to the multi-dimensional Lagrange expansion formula.

§13. See

R. BELLMAN and K. L. COOKE, *Differential-difference Equations*, Academic Press, New York, 1963.

§15. See

G. E. FORSYTHE and W. WASOW, *Finite Difference Methods for Partial Differential Equations*, John Wiley & Sons, New York, 1960.
for other approaches.

§17. See the book cited in the bibliography for Sec. 1.

§18. The basic idea of introducing a change of variable in the parameter is due to Shohat. See

J. SHOHAT, "On Van der Pol's and Related Nonlinear Differential Equations," *J. Appl. Phys.*, Vol. 15, 1944, pp. 568–574

R. BELLMAN, "On Perturbation Methods Involving Expansions in Terms of a Parameter," *Q. Appl. Math.*, Vol. 13, 1955, pp. 195–200.

———, "Perturbation Methods Applied to Nonlinear Mechanics," *Amer. Soc. Mech. Engrs.*, Paper No. 55-APM-33.

§20. For a discussion of functional equations of this type, see

L. MYSKIS, *Lineare Differentialgleichungen mit nacheilendem Argument*, Berlin, 1955.

§21. See

R. BELLMAN and R. KALABA, *Quasilinearization and Nonlinear Boundary-Value Problems*, American Elsevier, New York, 1965,

for a detailed account of the theory and application of quasilinearization. References to the Newton-Raphson-Kantorovich technique will be found there.

Chapter Five

DYNAMIC PROGRAMMING AND ILL-CONDITIONED SYSTEMS

1. INTRODUCTION

In the previous chapters, we obtained the numerical solution of various classes of functional equations by means of a multistage process. First, the Laplace transform

$$(1.1) \qquad \int_0^\infty e^{-st}u(t)\,dt = f(s)$$

was used to reduce the equation for $u(t)$ to a much simpler equation for $f(s)$. Then, we employed numerical quadrature to solve this linear integral equation for $u(t)$, given the values of $f(s)$. In this way, the ultimate problem was that of solving a system of linear algebraic equations of the form

$$(1.2) \qquad Ax = b.$$

An explicit determination of A^{-1} brought our work to a certain conclusion. In those cases where $f(s)$ can be determined to any required degree of accuracy, we can be quite confident of obtaining equally accurate values of $u(t)$.

As we have repeatedly pointed out, there are serious difficulties associated with a uniform application of this approach. The matrix A is ill-conditioned, reflecting the unboundedness of the Laplace inverse. This ill-conditionedness manifests itself in the behavior of A^{-1}. As N, the dimension of A, equal to the degree of the quadrature, increases, the elements of A increase rapidly in magnitude, and oscillate in sign; see Appendix Five.

It follows that a direct calculation of the solution of (1.2), using the formula $x = A^{-1}b$, can yield meaningless results if b is known to only a few significant figures. We shall give some examples of this. In many important applications, we meet precisely the problem of solving (1.2) under the conditions that A is ill-conditioned and b is known only to a limited accuracy. The methods we present are thus of wider applicability than that of Laplace inversion.

One of our prime motivations, however, is that of applying transform techniques to nonlinear functional equations. As we saw in Chapter Four, the application of quasilinearization automatically leads to linear systems where A^{-1} is not explicitly known. The situation occurs also when treating linear functional equations with time-varying coefficients.

The methods we present are applicable to the solution of more general linear integral equations of the form

$$(1.3) \qquad u(x) = f(x) + \int_a^b k(x,y)u(y)\,dy.$$

Although we shall give references to work by others in this area, we will not discuss this work directly.

The first part of the chapter treats the problem of solving (1.2) by using an auxiliary function

$$(1.4) \qquad (Ax - b, Ax - b) + \lambda\varphi(x),$$

where λ may be considered to be a Lagrange, or Courant, parameter and $\varphi(x)$ is a suitably chosen scalar function of the vector x. The choice of λ is critical for the success of the approach. In view of this criticality, it is natural to think of a technique of sequential computation in which the results of the first part of a computational algorithm are used to guide the choice of procedures in the second part.

This is consistent with the view of computational solution as an adaptive control process whose purpose is the minimization of overall error. Our work may be considered as an initial foray into this new and significant domain.

2. A LEAST SQUARES APPROACH

In some cases, the equation

(2.1) $$Ax = b$$

possesses no solution. This, for example, is often the situation if the number of equations is greater than the number of variables or if x must satisfy some supplementary conditions as well, such as non-negativity of elements. In these situations, it is meaningful to ask for the vector x minimizing the quadratic expression

(2.2) $$(Ax - b, Ax - b).$$

Here (x,y) denotes the inner product of two vectors, namely

(2.3) $$(x,y) = \sum_{i=1}^{N} x_i y_i.$$

In some cases, (2.1) is undetermined, in the sense that (2.1) possesses an infinity of solutions. In order to single out a desired solution, we consider, in place of (2.2), an expression of the form

(2.4) $$(Ax - b, Ax - b) + \lambda \varphi(x),$$

where φ is adroitly chosen.

Even in the case where A^{-1} exists, we may still possess difficulties from the numerical side. If b is known only to within an accuracy of ϵ, then (2.1) may be considered to define an equivalence class of vectors $\{x_i\}$ with the property that

(2.5) $$\|Ax_i - Ax_j\| \leq \epsilon.$$

If A is ill-conditioned, this need not, and in general, will not, imply that

(2.6) $$\|x_i - x_j\| \leq \epsilon,$$

or even 100ϵ. Here, a suitable norm is $(x,x)^{\frac{1}{2}}$.

The problem of overcoming or circumventing the instability of A^{-1} is always difficult and never routine. One cannot overemphasize the fact that no single approach, or combination of approaches, can be expected to be uniformly successful. What we wish to do in the following pages is to present an outline of some versatile new methods which appear promising.

Generally speaking, our attitude is that if one possesses additional information about the nature of the vector x satisfying (2.1), usually obtainable from the physical background of the problem, then we can take advantage of these clues to defeat the ill-mannered ill-conditionedness of A.

3. AN EXTRINSIC CONDITION

Let us begin with the case where we have already produced, in some fashion, an approximation to the desired vector x. Call this approximation c. In what follows, we shall indicate one way of obtaining c in connection with the Laplace inversion.

Consider then the modified problem of minimizing the quadratic function

$$(3.1) \qquad (Ax - b, Ax - b) + \lambda(x - c, x - c),$$

where λ is a nonnegative number. As might be expected, the choice of λ is of some import, and we shall have more to say about this below. An easy calculation shows that the vector which minimizes (3.1) is given by

$$(3.2) \qquad x(\lambda) = (A'A + \lambda I)^{-1}(A'b + \lambda c).$$

Here A' denotes the transpose of A. Various numerical experiments, plus analytic estimates, lead us to believe that $A'A + \lambda I$ is much less ill-conditioned than A even for quite small values of λ, although not in general for $\lambda = 0$. If λ is "small," we can expect $x(\lambda)$ to be an excellent approximation to the solution $Ax = b$.

It follows that one technique we can employ is to use any of a number of very efficient methods for solving linear algebraic equations to solve the linear system

$$(3.3) \qquad (A'A + \lambda I)x = A'b + \lambda c.$$

We shall, however, follow a different route. The minimization of (3.1) will be viewed as a multistage decision process, and the theory of dynamic programming will be employed to derive a computational algorithm. Apart from the interest attached to trying new techniques, this approach has the merit of being readily applicable to the minimization problems associated with different choices of $\varphi(x)$.

Furthermore, it serves as an introduction to the broad concept of numerical solution of equations as a multistage control process.

4. DYNAMIC PROGRAMMING APPROACH—I

To apply dynamic programming to the minimization of the quadratic function in (3.1), we convert the choice of the optimal x into a multistage process in the following way. First, we choose x_N, then x_{N-1}, and so on. In order to apply the functional equation approach, however, we must imbed the original problem within the more general problem of minimizing the quadratic expression

$$(4.1) \quad R_M(x) = \left[\lambda(x_1 - c_1)^2 + \lambda(x_2 - c_2)^2 + \cdots \right.$$
$$\left. + \lambda(x_M - c_M)^2 + \sum_{i=1}^{N} \left(\sum_{j=1}^{M} a_{ij}x_j - b_i \right)^2 \right],$$

where M may be any integer between 1 and N.

If $M = N$, we have the original problem; if $M = 1$, we have the simple problem of minimizing

$$(4.2) \qquad R_1(x) = \lambda(x_1 - c_1)^2 + \sum_{i=1}^{N} (a_{i1}x_1 - b_i)^2.$$

Our objective, then, is to obtain a recurrence relation connecting R_M with R_{M-1}.

Observe that in connection with minimizing $R_M(x)$, if we pick x_M, we are left with the problem of minimizing a function of the same type over $x_1, x_2, \ldots, x_{M-1}$ where only the values of the b_i have been changed. To be precise, if we set

$$(4.3) \qquad b = \begin{pmatrix} b_1 \\ b_2 \\ \cdot \\ \cdot \\ \cdot \\ b_N \end{pmatrix}, \qquad a^{(M)} = \begin{pmatrix} a_{1M} \\ a_{2M} \\ \cdot \\ \cdot \\ \cdot \\ a_{NM} \end{pmatrix},$$

a choice x_M transforms b into $b - x_M a^{(M)}$.

Hence, if we introduce the function

$$(4.4) \qquad f_M(b) = \min_{[x_1, x_2, \ldots, x_M]} R_M(x),$$

defined for $M = 1, 2, \ldots, N$ and all b, we obtain for $M \geq 2$ the recurrence relation

$$(4.5) \qquad f_M(b) = \min_{x_M} [\lambda(x_M - c_M)^2 + f_{M-1}(b - x_M a^{(M)})],$$

where

$$(4.6) \qquad f_1(b) = \min_{x_1} [R_1(x)].$$

The relation in (4.5) is an application of the principle of optimality.

5. DYNAMIC PROGRAMMING APPROACH—II

If the dimension of b were small, we could use (4.5) directly to obtain the numerical values of $\{f_M(b)\}$. If, however, N is large, it is essential to take advantage of the simple analytic structure of the function $f_M(b)$. We assert that $f_M(b)$ is for each M a quadratic function of b having the form

$$(5.1) \qquad f_M(b) = (b, Q_M b) + 2(p_M, b) + r_M,$$

where Q_M is a matrix independent of b, p_M is a vector independent of b and r_M is a scalar independent of b. To see this, note the form of the minimizing x, given by (3.3), a linear function of b. Substituting this in $R_M(x)$, we see that $f_M(b)$ has the stated form.

Using the recurrence relation of (4.5), some direct but laborious algebraic calculations enable us to obtain recurrence relations connecting (Q_M, p_M, r_M) with $(Q_{M-1}, p_{M-1}, r_{M-1})$, namely,

$$(5.2) \qquad Q_M = Q_{M-1} - \frac{A^{(M)}}{\lambda + K_M},$$

$$p_M = p_{M-1} - \frac{(\lambda c_M + \rho_M)\alpha^{(M)}}{(\lambda + K_M)},$$

$$r_M = r_{M-1} + \lambda c_M^2 - \frac{(\lambda c_M + \rho_M)^2}{(\lambda + K_M)},$$

where the auxiliary quantities in (5.2) are defined by

$$(5.3) \qquad \alpha^{(M)} = Q_{M-1} a^{(M)},$$

$$\rho_M = (p_{M-1}, a^{(M)}),$$

$$K_M = (\alpha^{(M)}, a^{(M)}),$$

and the matrix $A^{(M)}$ is given by

$$(5.4) \qquad A^{(M)} = \alpha^{(M)} \otimes \alpha^{(M)}.$$

Here $\otimes$ denotes the Kronecker product,

$$(5.5) \qquad a \otimes b = (a_i b_j), \qquad i, j = 1, 2, \ldots, N.$$

If we take

$$(5.6) \qquad Q_0 = I, \qquad p_0 = 0, \qquad r_0 = 0,$$

we can use the recurrence relation of (5.2) to obtain all of the Q_M, p_M, r_M for $M \geq 1$. This saves some programming and computing effort.

6. DETERMINATION OF THE MINIMIZING VALUES

To obtain the value of x that minimizes, we work forward and then backward. Starting with the values in (5.6), we determine the elements in the sequence (Q_M, p_M, r_M) for $M = 1, 2, \ldots, N$.

Having done this, we turn to the determination of x_M, x_{M-1}, $\ldots$, x_1. It is easily seen, using the representation of (5.1), that x_M, as determined by (4.5) is given by

$$(6.1) \qquad x_M = \frac{\lambda c_M + (p_{M-1}, a^{(M)}) + (a^{(M)}, Q_{M-1}b)}{\lambda + (a^{(M)}, Q_{M-1}a^{(M)})}.$$

Writing

$$(6.2) \qquad (a^{(M)}, Q_{M-1}b) = (Q_{M-1}a^{(M)}, b),$$

since Q_{M-1} is symmetric, we see that

$$(6.3) \qquad x_M = \frac{\lambda c_M + \rho_M + (\alpha^{(M)}, b)}{\lambda + K_M},$$

using the notation of (5.3). The vector $\alpha^{(M)}$ has already been calculated, as have also the quantities ρ_M and K_M. We are emphasizing these points since we want to avoid the storages of matrices.

To determine x_{M-1}, we must keep in mind that upon going from M to $M - 1$, b is replaced by $b - x_M a^{(M)}$. Hence

$$(6.4) \qquad x_{M-1} = \frac{\lambda c_{M-1} + \rho_{M-1} + (\alpha^{(M-1)}, b - x_M a^{(M-1)})}{\lambda + K_{M-1}}$$

$$= \frac{\lambda c_{M-1} + \rho_{M-1} + (\alpha^{M-1}, b) - x_M(\alpha^{(M-1)}, a^{(M-1)})}{\lambda + K_{M-1}}$$

$$= \frac{\lambda c_{M-1} + \rho_{M-1} + (\alpha^{M-1}, b) - x_M K_{M-1}}{\lambda + K_{M-1}}.$$

We can thus use the last expression, or we can use a program for the first line in (6.4). To determine x_{M-2}, we note that $b - x_M a^{(M-1)}$ is now replaced by $b - x_M a^{(M-1)} - x_{M-1} a^{(M-2)}$ and so on. This is the procedure we used in our computer program.

7. DISCUSSION

We can, of course, set $\lambda = 0$ and use this as a technique for solving the linear system $Ax = b$. With present rapid-access storage capacities, we can readily accommodate systems of dimension 100 or less.

However, if A is ill-conditioned, we can expect the same numerical instability as that encountered using conventional techniques. Examples given below illustrate this. Since the arithmetic is being done in a different fashion, one cannot assert which method will work more efficiently in general. It is probably best to carry out the calculations in parallel using a number of different algorithms. This is more and more common practice as large electronic computers become easily available.

In what follows, we wish to concentrate on various techniques of successive approximation and analytic continuation and on modifications of the variational formulation.

8. SUCCESSIVE APPROXIMATIONS

Let us now consider the situation where c is to be considered as an initial approximation, say x_1.* Then the x obtained as the minimizing value of

$$(8.1) \qquad (Ax - b, Ax - b) + \lambda(x - x_1, x - x_1)$$

may be considered a second approximation, x_2, and so on. Generally, we determine x_n as the vector minimizing

$$(8.2) \qquad (Ax - b, Ax - b) + \lambda(x - x_{n-1}, x - x_{n-1}).$$

To show that this process yields a convergent sequence for any $\lambda > 0$, we use the explicit representation of (3.2),

$$(8.3) \qquad x_n = (AA' + \lambda I)^{-1}A'b + \lambda(A'A + \lambda I)^{-1}x_{n-1}.$$

If A is nonsingular, as we shall suppose, then $A'A$ is symmetric and positive definite. Hence, all of the characteristic roots of $A'A + \lambda I$ are greater than λ, and all of the characteristic roots of $\lambda(A'A + \lambda I)^{-1}$ are positive and less than one. Thus, the sequence $\{x_n\}$ converges, and indeed geometrically.

---

* Not to be confused with the first component of x.

Let x be the limiting vector. Then

$$(8.4) \qquad (A'A + \lambda I)x = A'B + \lambda x$$

or

$$(8.5) \qquad A'Ax = A'b.$$

Since, by hypothesis, A' is nonsingular, we see that $Ax = b$.

Observe that in the choice of λ we are drawn simultaneously in two different directions. On the one hand, the choice of $\lambda = 0$ yields the most rapid convergence, namely, $x_2 = A^{-1}b$. However, if A is badly conditioned, $(AA')^{-1}$ will be impossible to obtain with any accuracy. On the other hand, if λ is large, $A'A + \lambda I$ will not be ill-conditioned, but the rate of convergence will be quite slow.

We shall discuss various ways of meeting these conflicting objectives.

9. OBTAINING AN INITIAL APPROXIMATION

In the previous chapter, we treated the inversion of the Laplace transform

$$(9.1) \qquad \int_0^\infty u(t)e^{-st}\,dt = f(s)$$

by using numerical quadrature. In place of (9.1), we faced a linear system of algebraic equations of the form

$$(9.2) \qquad \sum_{i=1}^{N} w_i u(t_i)e^{-st_i} = f(s), \qquad s = 1, 2, \ldots, N.$$

Here again, we found ourselves precariously perched on the horns of a dilemma: If N is large, the matrix of coefficients is so ill-conditioned that it is impossible to obtain $u(t_i)$ accurately; if N is small, the equations in (9.2) are not sufficiently precise to yield accurate values of $u(t_i)$.

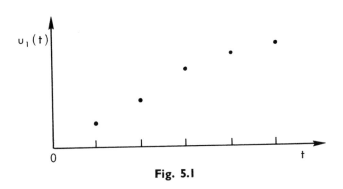

Fig. 5.1

Combining the solution for small N with the technique of the previous chapter, however, we can obtain accurate solutions, even when $f(s)$ is not very precisely given. For example, let (9.2) be solved for $N = 5$. (See Fig. 5.1.) Drawing a smooth curve through or near these points, usually computationally, that is, by means of an interpolation formula, we obtain an approximation to $u(t)$, say $u_1(t)$. (See Fig. 5.2.) Using this curve, we read off approximate values of $u_1(t_{iN})$, $i = 1, 2, \ldots, N$, where t_{iN} are the quadrature points for a larger value of N, say $N = 10$. These values $[u_1(t_{iN})]$ then constitute the first approximation x_1 in the method described in the foregoing sections. This idea will be extensively pursued below in a procedure possessing adaptive features.

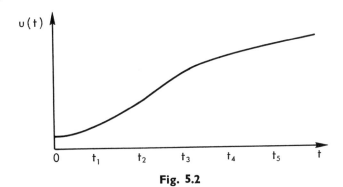

Fig. 5.2

In the more general case, where we face a linear integral equation of the form

$$(9.3) \qquad u(t) = g(t) + \int_0^1 k(t,t_1)u(t_1)\,dt_1,$$

we can begin with the equation

$$(9.4) \qquad u(t) = g(t) + \lambda \int_0^1 k(t,t_1)u(t_1)\,dt_1,$$

(where λ is the Poincaré parameter), and use the Liouville-Neumann solution for small λ. We can either use this to predict the value of the solution of (9.3), where $\lambda = 1$ or, as indicated in the previous chapter, expand in powers of $\lambda/(\lambda + \lambda_0)$, where λ_0 is suitably chosen. We shall pursue this idea of analytic continuation below.

In many cases, engineering and physical intuition and other mathematical formulations will furnish reasonable first approximations.

10. ANALYTIC CONTINUATION AND EXTRAPOLATION

Let us now present another approximate approach based upon the analytic structure of the minimizing value x. We know that the vector $x(\lambda)$ which yields the minimum of

$$(10.1) \qquad (Ax - b, Ax - b) + \lambda(x - c, x - c)$$

is given by

$$(10.2) \qquad x(\lambda) = (A'A + \lambda I)^{-1}(b + \lambda c).$$

In the neighborhood of $\lambda = 0$, this has a convergent power series expansion

$$(10.3) \qquad x(\lambda) = x_{\min} + \lambda y_1 + \lambda^2 y_2 + \cdots.$$

Furthermore, we know that $x(\lambda)$ is continuous and differentiable arbitrarily often for $\lambda > 0$.

It follows that we should be able to estimate the desired value of x_{min}, that is, $x(0)$, from values of $x(\lambda)$, obtained in other portions of the λ-plane. In particular, we wish to consider the case where $x(\lambda)$ can be obtained readily for λ positive and sufficiently large, in which case the matrix $A'A + \lambda I$ is not ill-conditioned. This estimate for x can once again be used as an initial approximation in the method described in the previous sections. In general, what we are suggesting is a combination of several techniques, rather than dependence upon a single approach. This is in line with the comments we have made above.

II. EXAMPLE

To illustrate the method in practice, consider the integral equation

$$(11.1) \qquad \int_0^1 (x - y)^2 u(y) \, dy = \frac{x^2}{2} - \frac{2x}{3} + \frac{1}{4},$$

where the right-hand side was chosen so that a solution is $u(y) = y$.

Let us use a quadrature formula, say Simpson's rule, with 11 equally spaced points, $y = 0, 0.1, 0.2, \ldots, 1$. Letting x assume these same values, we obtain a system of linear equations

$$(11.2) \qquad \sum_{j=1}^{11} a_{ij} x_j = b_i, \qquad i = 1, 2, \ldots, 11,$$

where $A = (a_{ij})$ and $b = (b_1, b_2, \ldots, b_{11})$ are known. The matrix A is not singular, but it is ill-conditoned.

In Table 5.1, we show the results of various choices of c and λ contrasted with the solution attempted by direct methods and the exact solution. It is clear that some additional effort is required to obtain a good approximation to the solution.

Figure 5.3 shows the instability of the solution obtained by matrix inversion using values of $g(x) = x^2/2 - 2x/3 + \frac{1}{4}$ accurate to eight significant figures. The solutions obtained by means of dynamic programming are shown in Fig. 5.4 for various values of λ using $g(x)$ accurate to only three significant figures.

Table 5.1

c	x	True	Inversion	$\lambda = 0$	0.01	0.05	0.1	0.15	0.2	0.25
0.0	0.0	0.0	−3.5010	−5.27970	0.03928	0.02937	0.02104	0.01629	0.01327	0.01118
0.05	0.1	0.1	4.6244	−0.54397	0.16775	0.13702	0.11247	0.09841	0.08946	0.08328
0.1	0.2	0.2	−24.9940	9.12340	0.14925	0.13476	0.12476	0.11914	0.11558	0.11313
0.15	0.3	0.3	8.9790	−12.36100	0.24924	0.21498	0.19535	0.18476	0.17816	0.17366
0.2	0.4	0.4	−4.2511	−24.51700	0.26024	0.23671	0.22498	0.21893	0.21524	0.21275
0.25	0.5	0.5	13.8760	64.63300	0.41172	0.34482	0.31333	0.29758	0.28811	0.28178
0.3	0.6	0.6	−9.7200	−71.49900	0.41155	0.36460	0.34274	0.33196	0.32553	0.32125
0.35	0.7	0.7	−4.5892	−36.84400	0.65464	0.52654	0.46639	0.43687	0.41931	0.40765
0.4	0.8	0.8	−9.3717	79.19900	0.60317	0.51843	0.47804	0.45822	0.44644	0.43862
0.45	0.9	0.9	2.7077	−7.72440	0.97820	0.76015	0.65454	0.60263	0.57175	0.55127
0.5	1.0	1.0	12.7820	1.79990	0.66755	0.59910	0.56544	0.54886	0.53899	0.53243

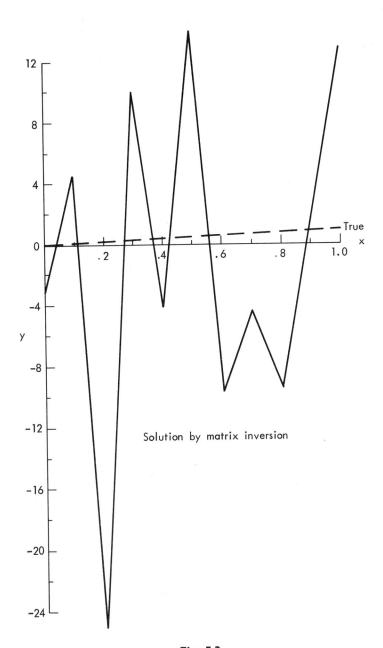

Fig. 5.3

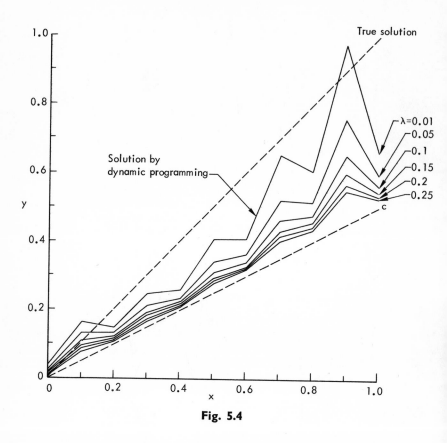

Fig. 5.4

12. APPLICATION OF SUCCESSIVE
APPROXIMATION PLUS SMOOTHING

To obtain better results, we turn to the method of successive approximations.

In Fig. 5.5, we see the result of forty iterations starting with an initial approximation corresponding to $a(y) = y/2$, with a value of $\lambda = 0.01$. Observe that the oscillations do not damp out in any strong fashion. If we continued the iteration, round-off error would soon eliminate any significance.

Let us then smooth the solution and use this smoothed vector as a

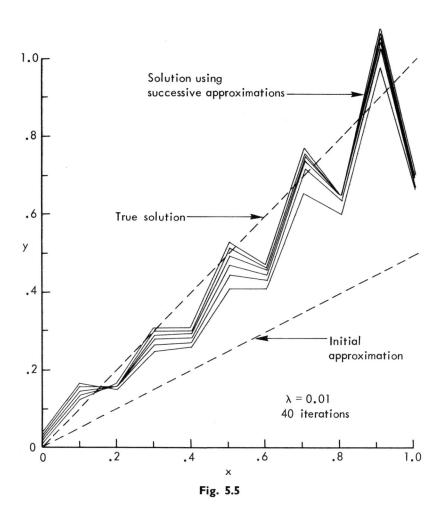

Fig. 5.5

new initial approximation. No sophistication was used in the smoothing. Figure 5.6 shows the great improvement in accuracy combined with a diminution of oscillation.

The process could be repeated several times and, indeed, made part of the original program. It is a simple example of the concept of sequential computation discussed in more detail in Sec. 18.

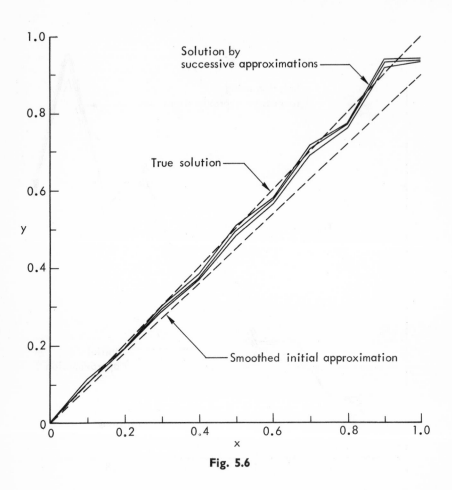

Fig. 5.6

13. RESULTS OF EXTRAPOLATION

Let us now apply the ideas of Sec. 10. In Fig. 5.7, we show the dependence of $x(\lambda)$ for a range of values of λ, where $x(\lambda)$ has been obtained using the foregoing dynamic programming algorithm. In Fig. 5.8, we show the relation of the extrapolated solution, where again no sophistication was used in the estimation of x_0, to the exact solution.

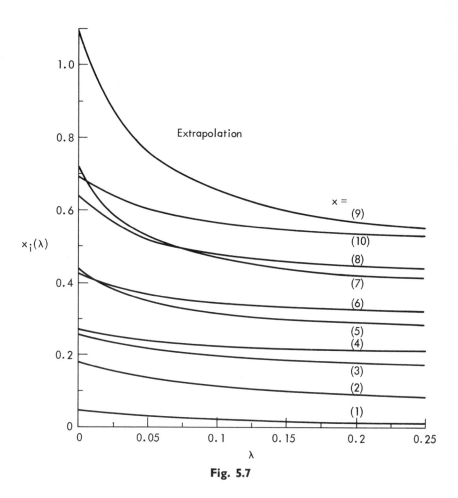

Fig. 5.7

Starting with the extrapolated estimate, as in Fig. 5.8, we could smooth, use the smoothed vector as an initial approximation, and so on.

14. A SELF-CONSISTENT METHOD

Our previous route was by way of the associated question of minimizing the quadratic expression

(14.1) $(Ax - b, Ax - b) + \lambda(x - c, x - c),$

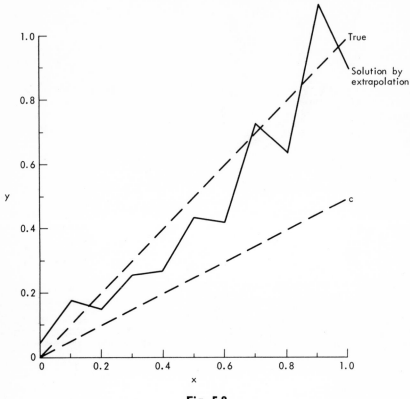

Fig. 5.8

where c is alternatively an initial approximation, or a known "nearby" vector.

Here we wish to use a self-consistent approach, aimed at those classes of linear equations where we know, from the origin of the problem, that there is a considerable degree of regularity and smoothness in the solution. In particular, we expect the expression

(14.2) $D_N(x) = (x_1 - x_2)^2 + (x_2 - x_3)^2 + \cdots + (x_{N-1} - x_N)^2$

to be fairly small. Here, as before, the x_i are the N components of the vector x. Consequently, in place of the expression in (3.1), we consider the associated function

(14.3) $(Ax - b, Ax - b) + \lambda D_N(x)$.

In these cases, we may not possess any information concerning an approximation to the solution.

We shall apply the functional-equation approach of dynamic programming to the minimization of this function, which involves a small amount of trickery, and then present some numerical results. We could also apply dynamic programming to treat the more general question of minimizing

(14.4) $\quad (Ax - b, Ax - b) + \lambda_1(x - c, x - c) + \lambda_2 D_N(x),$

under the assumption that we know an initial approximation c. However, the preliminary algebraic work becomes rather considerable, and we leave it to the reader himself to decide whether to carry this out.

15. DYNAMIC PROGRAMMING APPROACH

In order to obtain a simple recurrence relation, we consider first the problem of minimizing the function

(15.1) $\quad \sum_{i=1}^{M} \left(\sum_{j=2}^{N} a_{ij}x_j - z_i \right)^2 + \lambda[(x_N - x_{N-1})^2 + \cdots + (x_2 - c)^2]$

over $x_2, x_3, \ldots, x_N$, where the z_i and c are parameters. This minimum value we denote by $f_2(z,c)$, for fixed N. Once again, it is easy to see that it is a quadratic form in z and c. Having obtained this quadratic form, by means of a procedure we describe below, we replace M by N, c by x_1, z_1 by $b_i - a_{i1}x_1$, $i = 1, 2, \ldots, N$, and then minimize the resultant quadratic polynomial in x_1 over x_1. This yields the solution of the original minimization problem.

16. THE DETAILS

We begin with the introduction of the sequence of functions

(16.1) $\quad f_k(z,c) = \min_{x_r} \left[\sum_{i=1}^{M} \left(\sum_{j=k}^{N} a_{ij}x_j - z_i \right)^2 \right.$

$$\left. + \lambda[(x_N - x_{N-1})^2 + \cdots + (x_k - c)^2] \right],$$

where $r = k, k + 1, \ldots, N, k = 2, 3, \ldots, N$. We have

(16.2) $$f_N(z,c) = \underset{x_N}{\text{Min}} \left[\sum_{i=1}^{M} (a_{iN}x_N - z_i)^2 + \lambda(x_N - c)^2 \right],$$

and the principle of optimality yields the recurrence relation

(16.3) $$f_k(z,c) = \underset{x_k}{\text{Min}} \left[\lambda(x_k - c)^2 + f_{k+1}(z - a^k x_k, x_k) \right],$$

for $k = 2, 3, \ldots, N - 1$, where

(16.4) $$a^k = \begin{pmatrix} a_{1k} \\ a_{2k} \\ \cdot \\ \cdot \\ \cdot \\ a_{Mk} \end{pmatrix}$$

Using the fact that each function $f_k(z,c)$ is of the form

(16.5) $$f_k(z,c) = (z,Q_k z) + 2(z,P_k)c + r_k c^2,$$

and the recurrence relation of (16.3), we wish to find recurrence relations for the sequences $\{Q_k\}$, $\{P_k\}$ and $\{r_k\}$, a matrix, vector, and scalar sequence, respectively.

To solve for x_N we set the partial derivative of the term in brackets in (16.2) with respect to x_N equal to zero.

(16.6) $$0 = \lambda(x_N - c) + (a^N, a^N x_N - z)$$

$$x_N = \frac{\lambda c + (a^N, z)}{\lambda + (a^N, a^N)}$$

This yields the value of $f_N(z,c)$,

(16.7)

$$f_N(z,c) = -\lambda c(x_N - c) - (z, a^N x_N - z)$$

$$= \lambda c^2 + (z, Iz) - \lambda c \left[\frac{\lambda c + (a^N, z)}{\lambda + (a^N, a^N)} \right] - \left(z, a^N \left[\frac{\lambda c + (a^N, z)}{\lambda + (a^N, a^N)} \right] \right),$$

$$f_N(z,c) = c^2 \left(\lambda - \frac{\lambda^2}{\lambda + (a^N, a^N)} \right) + 2c \left(\frac{-\lambda(a^N, z)}{\lambda + (a^N, a^N)} \right)$$

$$+ \left(z, \left[I - \frac{A_N}{\lambda + (a^N, a^N)} \right] z \right),$$

where

$$(16.8) \qquad A_N = a^N \otimes a^N,$$

$\otimes$ denoting the Kronecker product,

$$(16.9) \qquad x \otimes y = (x_i y_j), \qquad i, j = 1, 2, \ldots, N.$$

Since $f_N(z,c)$ can be expressed in quadratic form as

$$(16.10) \qquad f_N(z,c) = (z, Q_N z) + 2c(z, P_N) + r_N c^2,$$

$$Q_N = I - \frac{A_N}{\lambda + (a^N, a^N)},$$

$$(16.11) \qquad P_N = -\frac{\lambda a^N}{\lambda + (a^N, a^N)}, \quad \text{and}$$

$$r_N = \frac{\lambda (a^N, a^N)}{\lambda + (a^N, a^N)}.$$

In order to obtain the recurrence relationships, we find x_{N-1} and $f_{N-1}(z,c)$ in the same way.

(16.12)

$$f_{N-1}(z,c) = \operatorname*{Min}_{x_{N-1}} [\lambda(x_{N-1} - c)^2 + f_N(z - a^{N-1} x_{N-1}, x_{N-1})]$$

$$= \operatorname*{Min}_{x_{N-1}} [\lambda(x_{N-1} - c)^2 + (z - a^{N-1} x_{N-1}, Q_N(z - a^{N-1} x_{N-1}))$$

$$+ 2(P_N, (z - a^{N-1} x_{N-1}))x_{N-1} + r_N x_{N-1}^2].$$

Again, we set the partial derivative of (16.12) equal to zero and solve for x_{N-1}.

$$(16.13) \quad 0 = \lambda(x_{N-1} - c) - (a^{N-1}, Q_N(z - a^{N-1} x_{N-1}))$$

$$+ (P_N, (z - a^{N-1} x_{N-1})) - (P_N, a^{N-1} x_{N-1}) + r_N x_{N-1}$$

$$= x_{N-1}[\lambda + (a^{N-1}, Q_N a^{N-1}) - 2(P_N, a^{N-1}) + r_N]$$

$$- [\lambda c + (a^{N-1}, Q_N z) - (P_N, z)]$$

$$x_{N-1} = \frac{\lambda c + (a^{N-1}, Q_N z) - (P_N, z)}{\lambda + (a^{N-1}, Q_N a^{N-1}) - 2(P_N, a^{N-1}) + r_N}.$$

We now define

(16.14)
$$\alpha^N = Q_N a^{N-1},$$

$$\rho^N = (P_N, a^{N-1}), \quad \text{and}$$

$$K_N = (a^{N-1}, \alpha^N).$$

Equation (16.13) can now be written

(16.15)
$$x_{N-1} = \frac{\lambda c + (\alpha^N, z) - (P_N, z)}{\lambda + K_N - 2\rho_N + r_N}.$$

Substituting (16.15) in (16.12) we obtain

(16.16)

$$f_{N-1}(z,c) = (z, Q_{N-1}z) + 2(P_N, z)c + r_{N-1}c^2$$

$$= \lambda c^2 - \lambda c x_N + (z, Q_N z) - (z, Q_N a^{N-1} x_{N-1}) + (P_N x_N, z)$$

$$= (z, Q_N z) + \lambda c^2 - \left[\frac{\lambda^2 c^2 + \lambda c(\alpha^N, z) - \lambda c(P_N, z)}{\lambda + K_N - 2\rho_N + r_N} \right]$$

$$- \left(z, \alpha^N \left[\frac{\lambda c + (\alpha^N, z) - (P_N, z)}{\lambda + K_N - 2\rho_N + r_N} \right] \right)$$

$$+ \left(P_N, z \left[\frac{\lambda c + (\alpha^V, z) - (P_N, z)}{\lambda + K_N - 2\rho_N + r_N} \right] \right)$$

$$f_{N-1}(z,c) = (z, Q_{N-1}z) + 2(P_{N-1}, z)c + r_{N-1}c^2 = (z, Q_N z)$$

$$- \frac{1}{\lambda + K_N - 2\rho_N + r_N} (\alpha^N - P_N, z)^2$$

$$+ 2c \left[\frac{\lambda}{\lambda + K_N - 2\rho + r_N} (P_N - \alpha^N, z) \right]$$

$$+ c^2 \lambda \left(\frac{K_N - 2\rho_N + r_N}{\lambda + K_N - 2\rho_N + r_N} \right).$$

From (16.16) we obtain the following recurrence relationships

$$(16.17) \quad Q_{N-1} = Q_N - \frac{1}{\lambda + K_N - 2\rho_N + r_N} (\alpha^N - P_N) \otimes (\alpha^N - P_N),$$

$$P_{N-1} = \frac{\lambda}{\lambda + K_N - 2\rho_N + r_N} (P_N - \alpha^N), \quad \text{and}$$

$$r_{N-1} = \frac{\lambda(K_N - 2\rho_N + r_N)}{\lambda + K_N - 2\rho_N + r_N}.$$

The computational scheme is as follows: Q_N, P_N, and r_N are computed from the inputs obtained from (16.2); Q_{N-1}, P_{N-1}, and r_{N-1} are then computed from the recurrence relationships (16.17). This process is repeated until Q_1, P_2, and r_2 are calculated. From these we can determine x_1 by minimizing the quadratic polynomial of (16.5) over c. Replacing c and x_1, and z by $b - a^1x_1$, we find x_2. We then replace c by x_2 and z by $b - a^2x_2$ and repeat until all the x_N have been found.

17. EXAMPLE

The equation used in the previous Secs. 11–13 was chosen to demonstrate the method described above. The equation we consider is

$$(17.1) \qquad \int_0^1 (x - y)^2 u(y) \, dy = \frac{x^2}{2} - \frac{2x}{3} + \frac{1}{4}.$$

We wish to single out the smooth, nonunique solution $u(y) = y$.

The quadrature method used was again Simpson's Rule, with 11 equally spaced points $y = 0, 0.1, 0.2, \ldots, 1.0$. Allowing x to assume these same values, we obtain the linear system

$$(17.2) \qquad \sum_{j=1}^{11} a_{ij}x_j = b_i, \qquad i = 1, 2, \ldots, 11,$$

where the matrix $A = (a_{ij})$ and the vector $b = (b_1, b_2, \ldots, b_N)$ are known.

Figure 5.9 shows the expected instability of the system where a method using reduction to Jordan canonical form was employed.

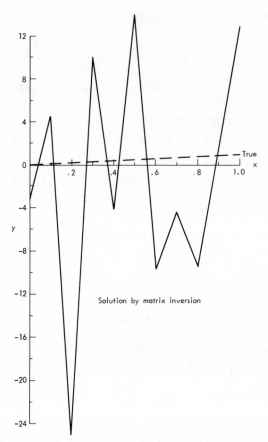

Fig. 5.9—Solution by matrix inversion

Figure 5.10 shows the results of this method if the right-hand side is accurate to three significant figures. Figures 5.11 and 5.12 show results when even less accuracy is used in the right-hand sides.

18. SEQUENTIAL COMPUTATION

Let us now pursue the idea sketched in Sec. 14. Consider the problem of obtaining a numerical inversion of the Laplace transform

$$(18.1) \qquad \int_0^\infty u(t)e^{-st}\, dt = f(s)$$

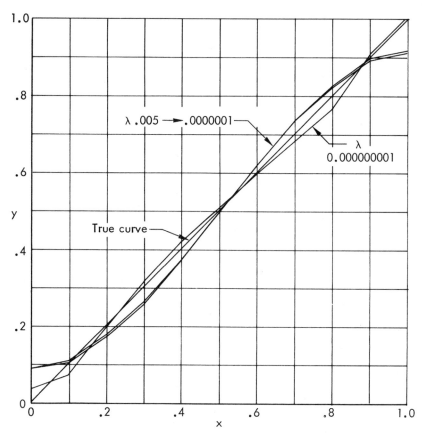

Fig. 5.10—Solution using dynamic programming, three-figure accuracy on right-hand side

in the case where $f(s)$ is known to a limited degree of accuracy. As we have pointed out several times before, a low-order quadrature formula will automatically yield a low order of accuracy, while a high-order quadrature formula will yield completely wild results. To illustrate this, consider the case where $f(s) = 1/(s + \frac{1}{2})$, $u(t) = e^{-t/2}$. If we use a nine-point quadrature formula, eight significant figures in the values of $f(s)$, and a standard technique for solving linear algebraic equations, we obtain the results shown in Table 5.2.

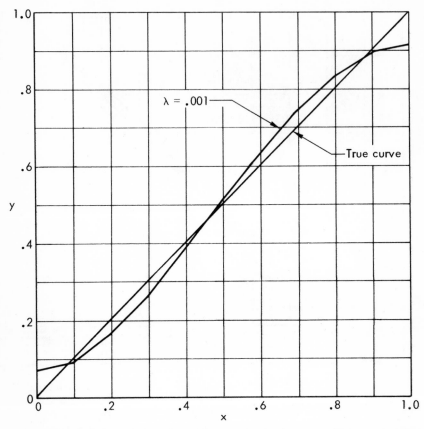

Fig. 5.11—Solution using dynamic programming, two-figure accuracy on right-hand side

The column headed "Exact $u(t)$" contains the values of $e^{-t/2}$ to eight significant figures. The other column contains the values obtained from the computational algorithm. The agreement is all that could be desired.

If, on the other hand, we use an input for $f(s)$ of five significant figures, we see that the algorithm produces a badly distorted solution; see Table 5.3. Were we to use only three significant figures, the distortion would increase greatly; see Table 5.4.

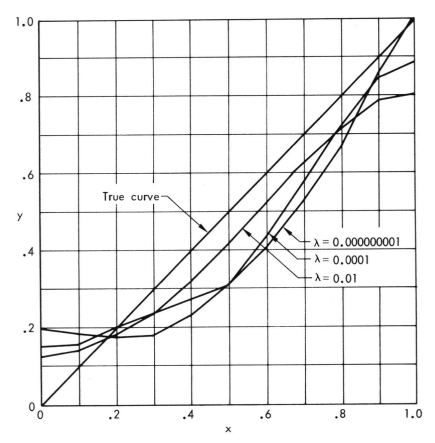

Fig. 5.12—Solution using dynamic programming, one-figure accuracy on right-hand side

To escape this quandary, we can proceed as follows. Let us use a low-order quadrature formula, say $N = 3$, to obtain a set of values $\{u(t_{i3})\}$, $i = 1, 2, 3$, where $r = e^{-t_{i5}}$ are the three roots of the shifted Legendre polynomial, $P_3^*(r)$. We suppose that these values are within a few percent of the actual values and that we want both more values and more precision. The Lagrange interpolation formula,

$$(18.2) \qquad v(r) = \sum_{i=1}^{3} \frac{P_3^*(r)}{(r - r_i)P_3^{*'}(r_i)}$$

Table 5.2*

t	$u(t)$		Exact $u(t)$	
4.140186	0.120527	00	0.126176	00
2.501226	0.288195	00	0.286329	00
1.643438	0.439084	00	0.439675	00
1.085084	0.581308	00	0.581269	00
0.693147	0.707318	00	0.707107	00
0.412298	0.813401	00	0.813712	00
0.214821	0.898482	00	0.898157	00
0.085541	0.957847	00	0.958131	00
0.016048	0.992205	00	0.992008	00

Table 5.3

t	$u(t)$		Exact $u(t)$	
4.140186	0.552507	00	0.126174	00
2.501226	−0.394986	00	0.286329	00
1.643438	0.132527	01	0.439675	00
1.085084	−0.434618	00	0.581269	00
0.693147	0.175839	01	0.707107	00
0.412298	−0.187608	00	0.813712	00
0.214821	0.178522	01	0.898157	00
0.085541	0.238746	00	0.958131	00
0.016048	0.147245	01	0.992008	00

Table 5.4

t	$u(t)$		Exact $u(t)$	
4.140186	0.932487	02	0.126174	00
2.501226	−0.137352	03	0.286329	00
1.643438	0.163960	03	0.439675	00
1.085084	−0.172213	03	0.581269	00
0.693147	0.168396	03	0.707107	00
0.412298	−0.151717	03	0.813712	00
0.214821	0.131910	03	0.898157	00
0.085541	−0.103282	03	0.958131	00
0.016048	0.699390	02	0.992008	00

* The notation . . . 01 indicates that the printed value is to be multiplied by 10; the notation . . . −02 indicates multiplication by 10^{-2} and so on.

yields a convenient way of obtaining a set of approximate values of $u(\log 1/r)$ at the five points r_1, r_2, r_3, r_4, r_5, the zeros of $P_5^*(r)$. These five values can then be used as an initial approximation c in the minimization of

$$(18.3) \qquad (Ax - b, Ax - b) + \lambda(x - c, x - c),$$

where $Ax = b$ is the equation derived by use of the five-point quadrature formula. We continue, using successive approximations as discussed above, and in this way find a set of values $\{u(t_{i5})\}$, $i = 1, 2, 3, 4, 5$.

The Lagrange interpolation formula for five points is now used to generate an initial seven-point solution, and so on. Let us mention in passing that if we know that the solution is smoother than what a low-order polynomial approximation will yield, we can use in place of (18.2) a spline approximation. Generally, it would be quite worthwhile to devote a considerable amount of effort to as sophisticated an interpolation formula as possible, using *a priori* knowledge of the value of $u(t)$ at $t = 0$, the asymptotic form as $t \to \infty$, and so on. Throughout this book, we have reiterated the theme that our techniques can be significantly refined in the study of any particular problem.

Attractive as the foregoing procedure is, it cannot be applied routinely. The choice of λ is vital. If λ is too large, the minimizing vector does not deviate significantly from c, the initial approximation. If λ is too small, the initial approximation plays an insignificant role, and we end up with a vector which renders $(Ax - b, Ax - b)$ small, but which deviates considerably from c.

How do we choose an appropriate value of λ?

Let us proceed in the following fashion. Starting with $N = 3$, or some larger value if we have sufficient confidence, let us turn to the minimization of the expression in (18.3) allowing λ to assume a spread of values λ_1, λ_2, ..., λ_M. Let $x^{(1)}$, $x^{(2)}$, ..., $x^{(M)}$ denote the corresponding vectors obtained by the method described in the earlier sections, a combination of dynamic programming and successive approximations.

We call a vector *acceptable* if $(x - c, x - c) \leq \epsilon$, where ϵ is an input parameter. Let $\{x^{(j)}\}$ denote the set of acceptable parameters. This set may be empty if ϵ is chosen to be quite small. We can, however, as was pointed out above, ensure that the set is not empty by including sufficiently large values of λ.

If the set is not empty, let x_m denote the vector in this set which minimizes $(Ax - b, Ax - b)$. This minimum value is referred to below as MSD = mean square deviation. This vector is used in connection with the Lagrange interpolation formula to obtain a new c for the next higher-dimensional quadrature formula, and so on.

In the following section, we give the results of the application of this sequential procedure for the case of inputs of both eight and five significant figures, starting with $N = 3$, and continuing through 5, 7, and 9. In Appendix One, we exhibit a FORTRAN program for this algorithm.

19. AN EXAMPLE

We take the case previously considered where $u(t) = e^{-t/2}$, $f(s) = 1/(s + \frac{1}{2})$ and consider first the case where $f(s)$ is known to eight significant figures and then five significant figures.

For $N = 3$, we have, as a result of three-point quadrature:

$t = -\log r$	$u(t)$
0.21830111 01	0.31873282
0.69314718	0.71428567
0.11957401	0.93841009

For $N = 5$, we have the initial approximation via quadrature and the result obtained using the dynamic programming algorithm together with an optimal choice of λ. We choose $\epsilon = 10^{-4}$ and use the following values of λ: 0, 10^{-9}, 10^{-7}, 10^{-5}, 10^{-3}, 10^{-2}, 0.1, 1.

$t = -\log r$		$u(t)$ Interpolation	$u(t)$ Algorithm	$\lambda = 0.1$
0.30595228	01	0.23450501	0.23529975	
0.14663539	01	0.45747668	0.45761404	
0.69314718		0.71428566	0.71223254	
0.26235921		0.88825209	0.88836647	
0.48046022	−01	0.95944876	0.96261908	
		MSD = 0.45326192 −06	MSD = 0.15745373 −06	

For N = 7,

$t = -\log r$		$u(t)$ Interpolation	$u(t)$ Algorithm	$\lambda = 0.1$
0.36711950	01	0.20654511	0.20756897	
0.20461274	01	0.34003266	0.34172137	
0.12137625	01	0.52783936	0.52840947	
0.69314718		0.71223254	0.71005522	
0.35250853		0.85224324	0.84957986	
0.13838246		0.93419250	0.93612928	
0.25775394	−01	0.96869803	0.97265887	
		MSD = 0.80370843 −06	MSD = 0.31779958 −06	

For N = 9,

$t = -\log r$		$u(t)$ Interpolation	$u(t)$ Algorithm	$\lambda = 0.1$
0.41401866	01	0.19443091	0.19508607	
0.25012257	01	0.28259712	0.28396942	
0.16434380	01	0.41713848	0.41870725	
0.10850843	01	0.56864519	0.56936462	
0.69314718		0.71005522	0.70878569	
0.41229833		0.82457412	0.82168892	
0.21482113		0.90640327	0.90505540	
0.85540946	−01	0.95482862	0.95756578	
0.16047963	−01	0.97507860	0.97841889	
		MSD = 0.76223251 −06	MSD = 0.34014083 −06	

The results are rather disappointing, as compared say to the results given in Table 5.2 in Sec. 18. We don't understand why the dynamic programming algorithm gives results of such poor accuracy.

When, however, we turn to the input with only five significant
figures, then the dynamic programming-interpolation algorithm
yields results far superior to those obtained by a straightforward
attempt to solve the linear system $Ax = b$ in the nine-point quadrature case.

Thus, we find, corresponding to the foregoing sets of values,

$t = -\log r$	$u(t)$
0.21830111	0.3188123
0.69314718	0.7142001
0.11957401	0.93842768

The results obtained from the three-point quadrature case are
equal to three significant figures to those obtained previously. For
$N = 5$, we have

$t = -\log r$		$u(t)$ Interpolation	$u(t)$ Algorithm	$\lambda = 0.1$
0.30595228	01	0.23463554	0.23541992	
0.14663539	01	0.45748256	0.45761608	
0.69314718		0.71421000	0.71218267	
0.26235921		0.88821493	0.88833068	
0.48046022	−01	0.95950688	0.96263614	
		MSD = 0.44125451 −06	MSD = 0.15266729	−06

For $N = 7$, we have

$t = -\log r$		$u(t)$ Interpolation	$u(t)$ Algorithm	$\lambda = 0.1$
0.36711950	01	0.20668643	0.20770048	
0.20461274	01	0.34008750	0.34175955	
0.12137625	01	0.52781921	0.52838287	
0.69314718		0.71218267	0.71002468	
0.35250853		0.85219873	0.84955896	
0.13838246		0.93417946	0.93610037	
0.25775394	−01	0.96872515	0.9726539	
		MSD = 0.79037652 −06	MSD = 0.31243516	−06

For $N = 9$, we have

$t = -\log r$		$u(t)$ Interpolation	$u(t)$ Algorithm	$\lambda = 0.1$
0.41401866	01	0.19457410	0.19522382	
0.25012257	01	0.28267097	0.28403180	
0.16434380	01	0.41714223	0.41869790	
0.10850843	01	0.56861324	0.56932709	
0.69314718		0.71002468	0.70876615	
0.41229833		0.82455334	0.83169024	
0.21482113		0.90637678	0.90503760	
0.85540946	-01	0.95480381	0.95752069	
0.16047963	-01	0.97507947	0.97839697	
		MSD $= 0.75130227$ -06	MSD $= 0.33541162$ -06	

If we use the following choices of λ: 0.02, 0.04, 0.06, 0.08, 0.09, 0.1, 0.11, 0.12, 0.15, 0.20, 0.30, 0.40, we end up with the following results for the case $N = 9$, and an input of eight significant figures:

$t = -\log r$		$u(t)$ Interpolation	$u(t)$ Algorithm	$\lambda = 0.1$
0.41401866	01	0.19457488	0.19367909	
0.25012257	01	0.28454977	0.28359243	
0.16434380	01	0.42044424	0.42099434	
0.10850843	01	0.57093524	0.57295142	
0.69314718		0.70853024	0.70947842	
0.41229833		0.81990218	0.81756814	
0.21482113		0.90355571	0.90081903	
0.85540946	-01	0.95730120	0.95916793	
0.16047963	-01	0.98144083	0.98503854	
		MSD $= 0.22068072$ -06	MSD $= 0.11482326$ -06	

If we use an input of five significant figures, we obtain

$t = -\log r$		$u(t)$ Interpolation	$u(t)$ Algorithm	$\lambda = 0.1$
0.41401866	01	0.19472316	0.19383496	
0.25012257	01	0.28460893	0.28365964	
0.16434380	01	0.42041471	0.42096112	
0.10850843	01	0.57087991	0.57288390	
0.69314718		0.70851430	0.70945965	
0.41229833		0.81992354	0.81760163	
0.21482113		0.90355706	0.90082870	
0.85540946	−01	0.95725676	0.95911501	
0.16047963	−01	0.98137653	0.98496334	
		MSD = 0.21832695 −06	MSD = 0.11331400	−06

If we use a value of $\epsilon = 10^{-3}$ with an input of eight significant figures, we obtain the following for $N = 3$

$t = -\log r$		$u(t)$
0.21830111	01	0.31873282
0.69314718		0.71428567
0.11957401		0.93841009

For $N = 5$, we have

$t = -\log r$		$u(t)$ Interpolation	$u(t)$ Algorithm	$\lambda = 0.1$
0.30595228	01	0.23450501	0.22502456	
0.14663539	01	0.45747668	0.46708793	
0.69314718		0.71428566	0.71405613	
0.26235921		0.88825209	0.87541260	
0.48046022	−01	0.95944876	0.97604816	
		MSD = 0.45326192 −06	MSD = 0.91379604	−08

For $N = 7$,

$t = -\log r$		$u(t)$ Interpolation	$u(t)$ Algorithm	$\lambda = 0.1$
0.36711950	01	0.19247928	0.17195013	
0.20461274	01	0.34146524	0.34159240	
0.12137625	01	0.53886899	0.55626965	
0.69314718		0.71405613	0.70452338	
0.35250853		0.83988087	0.83530632	
0.13838246		0.92934269	0.93827280	
0.25775394	−01	0.98910854	0.98293781	
		MSD $= 0.18472169$ −07	MSD $= 0.36868955$ −10	

For $N = 9$,

$t = -\log r$		$u(t)$ Interpolation	$u(t)$ Algorithm	$\lambda = 0.1$
0.41401866	01	0.15715532	0.14050499	
0.25012257	01	0.26457701	0.26829074	
0.16434380	01	0.43631527	0.44966527	
0.10850843	01	0.59278679	0.58012563	
0.69314718		0.70452338	0.70366907	
0.41229833		0.80796023	0.81781154	
0.21482113		0.90244644	0.89513044	
0.85540946	−01	0.96053009	0.95990407	
0.16047963	−01	0.98642337	0.99113321	
		MSD $= 0.78801474$ −09	MSD $= 0.60910500$ −12	

Using a value of $\epsilon = 10^{-3}$ with an input of five significant figures, we obtain for $N = 3$:

$t = -\log r$		$u(t)$
0.21830111	01	0.31881231
0.69314718		0.71421001
0.11957401		0.93842768

For $N = 5$,

$t = -\log r$		$u(t)$ Interpolation	$u(t)$ Algorithm	$\lambda = 0.1$
0.30595228	01	0.23463554	0.22534261	
0.14663539	01	0.45748256	0.46694841	
0.69314718		0.71421000	0.71392612	
0.26235921		0.88821493	0.87563524	
0.48046022	−01	0.95950688	0.97581743	
		MSD = 0.44125451 −06	MSD = 0.89124068	−08

For $N = 7$,

$t = -\log r$		$u(t)$ Interpolation	$u(t)$ Algorithm	$\lambda = 0.1$
0.36711950	01	0.19286677	0.17247746	
0.20461274	01	0.34154081	0.34218159	
0.12137625	01	0.53865358	0.55505011	
0.69314718		0.71892612	0.70494810	
0.35250853		0.84006073	0.83598049	
0.13838246		0.92945324	0.93705378	
0.25775394	−01	0.98873937	0.98390555	
		MSD = 0.19526800 −07	MSD = 0.82154058	−10

For $N = 9$,

$t = -\log r$		$u(t)$ Interpolation	$u(t)$ Algorithm	$\lambda = 0.1$
0.41401866	01	0.15741489	0.14666068	
0.25012257	01	0.26560346	0.26627619	
0.16434380	01	0.43596794	0.44587242	
0.10850843	01	0.59161880	0.58580067	
0.69314718		0.70494810	0.69978088	
0.41229833		0.80897330	0.81764625	
0.21482113		0.90175040	0.89961560	
0.85540946	−01	0.95963559	0.95304018	
0.16047963	−01	0.98792203	0.99695230	
		MSD = 0.47098645 −09	MSD = 0.32372469	−10

BIBLIOGRAPHY AND COMMENTS

§1.   A considerable amount of effort has been devoted to the problem of solving $Ax = b$ when A is ill-conditioned. Let us merely cite the following papers which are closest in spirit to the material in the text:

D. L. PHILLIPS, "A Technique for the Numerical Solution of Certain Integral Equations of the First Kind," *J. Assoc. Computing Machinery*, Vol. 9, 1962, pp. 84–97.

S. TWOMEY, "On the Numerical Solution of Fredholm Integral Equations of the First Kind by the Inversion of the Linear System Produced by Quadrature," *J. Assoc. Computing Machinery*, Vol. 10, 1963, pp. 97–101.

W. OETTLI and W. PRAEGER, "Compatibility of Approximate Solution of Linear Equations with Given Error Bounds for Coefficients and Right-hand Sides," *Numerische Mathematik*, Vol. 6, 1964, pp. 405–409.

A. N. TIHONOV, "On the Solution of Ill-posed Problems and the Method of Regularization," *Doklady Akad. Nauk SSSR*, Vol. 151, 1963, pp. 501–504; Vol. 153, 1963, pp. 49–52.

A. N. TIHONOV and V. B. GLASKO, "An Approximate Solution of Fredholm Integral Equations of the First Kind," *Zhurnal vychislitel'noy matematiki i matematicheskoy Fiziki*, Vol. 4, 1964, pp. 564–571.

For a general discussion with many references, see

G. E. FORSYTHE, "Solving Linear Algebraic Equations Can be Interesting," *Bull. Amer. Math. Soc.*, Vol. 59, 1953, pp. 299–329.

§4.   For the background of dynamic programming, see

R. BELLMAN, *Dynamic Programming*, Princeton University Press, Princeton, New Jersey, 1957.

R. BELLMAN and S. DREYFUS, *Applied Dynamic Programming*, Princeton University Press, Princeton, New Jersey, 1962.

R. BELLMAN, *Adaptive Control Processes: A Guided Tour*, Princeton University Press, Princeton, New Jersey, 1961.

See also Chapter 9 of

R. BELLMAN, *Introduction to Matrix Analysis*, McGraw-Hill, New York, 1960.

These results were originally presented in

R. BELLMAN, R. KALABA, and J. LOCKETT, "Dynamic Programming and Ill-conditioned Linear Systems," *J. Math. Anal. & Appl.*, Vol. 10, 1965, pp. 206–215.

———, "Dynamic Programming and Ill-conditioned Linear Systems—II," *J. Math. Anal. & Appl.*, Vol. 12, 1965, pp. 393–400.

§7.   See

R. S. LEHMAN, "Dynamic Programming and Gaussian Elimination," *J. Math. Anal. Appl.*, Vol. 5, 1962, pp. 499–501.

FORTRAN IV PROGRAMS

I. THE HEAT EQUATIONS

The following programs are listed:

HEAT   main program

INCON   subroutine

COEFF   subroutine

DAUX   subroutine

INPUT   subroutine

EXPINV   subroutine

The following subroutine is needed:

RWINT   subroutine*

* Causey, R., and W. L. Frank, *Adams-Moulton, Runge-Kutta Integration Subroutine*, Space Technology Laboratories, SHARE Routine Number 602; adapted by W. L. Sibley and F. Valadez, The RAND Corporation.

```
$IBFTC HEAT
C
C      SOLUTION OF HEAT EQUATION BY MEANS OF THE LAPLACE TRANSFORM
C
C      DIMENSION
C
           DIMENSION T(363),Y(30),V(15),W2(15),T1(15),A(15,15),R(15
    115)  ,W1(15),C(15)
C
C      DOUBLE PRECISION
C
           DOUBLE PRECISION A,R,W,W1,C,T1
C
C      COMMON
C
           COMMON T,IS,K1,A2,A3,A4,A5,A6,A7,C1,X,H,XMAX,V,W2,XK
C
C      INPUT
C
           READ(5,1)K1,K2,X,H,XMAX
           READ(5,2)A2,A3,A4,A5,A6,A7
           CALL INPUT(IS,R,W,T1)
           CALL EXPINV(IS,R,W,A)
           WRITE(6,102)(R(I),I=1,IS)
           WRITE(6,103)(W(I),I=1,IS)
           WRITE(6,104)
           DO 7 I=1,IS
    7      WRITE(6,105)(A(I,J),J=1,IS)
           WRITE(6,108)(T1(I),I=1,IS)
           PI=3.14159265
C
C      LAPLACE TRANSFORM
C
           CALL INCON
           I2S=2*IS
           DO 32 I=1,IS
           Y(2*I-1)=0.0
    32     Y(2*I)=-V(I)/W2(I)
           DO 110 I=4,363
    110    T(I)=0.0
           DO 33 I=1,I2S
    33     T(I+3)=Y(I)
           T(2)=X
           T(3)=H
           CALL COEFF(XX)
           XK=XX
           WRITE(6,101)XK
           WRITE(6,200)(V(I),I=1,IS)
           WRITE(6,201)(W2(I),I=1,IS)
           C1=-XK*SIN(T(2)*PI)
           CALL INTS(T,I2S,K1,A2,A3,A4,A5,A6,A7)
    37     DO 34 J=1,K2
           CALL COEFF(XX)
```

```
              XK=XX
              C1=-XK*SIN(T(2)*PI)
   34         CALL INTM
              DO 35 I=1,IS
   35         W1(I)=T(2*I+2)
              WRITE(6,106)T(2),(W1(I),I=1,IS)
C
C      INVERSION
C
              DO 40 I=1,IS
              C(I)=0.0D0
              DO 40 J=1,IS
   40         C(I)=C(I)+A(I,J)*W1(J)
   36         WRITE(6,107)T(2),(C(I),I=1,IS)
              IF(ABS(T(2)-XMAX).GT.T(3)/2.)GO TO 37
              CALL EXIT
C
C      FORMATS
C
    1 FORMAT(2I12,3E12.8)
    2 FORMAT(6E12.8)
  101 FORMAT(//5X16HVALUE OF K(X) = ,F5.2)
  102 FORMAT(1H1,5X29HROOTS                              /(5X6D20.8))
  103 FORMAT(//5X30HWEIGHTS                            /(5X6D20.8))
  104 FORMAT(//5X16HEXPLICIT INVERSE/)
  105 FORMAT(5X6D20.8)
  108 FORMAT(//5X30HT = -LOG R                         /(5X6D20.8))
  200 FORMAT(//5X32HV(I)                               /(5X6E20.8))
  201 FORMAT(//5X32HW2(I)                              /(5X6E20.8))
  106 FORMAT(//5X34HVALUE OF LAPLACE TRANSFORM AT X = ,F5.2 /(5X6D20.8))
  107 FORMAT(//5X33HINVERSE LAPLACE TRANSFORM AT X = ,F5.2 /(5X6D20.8))
              END
```

```
$IBFTC INCON
              SUBROUTINE INCON
C
C      DIMENSION
C
              DIMENSION T(363),Y(30),V(15),W2(15)
C
C      COMMON
C
              COMMON T,IS,K1,A2,A3,A4,A5,A6,A7,C1,X,H,XMAX,V,W2,XK
C
C      CALCULATE V(I)
C
              I2S=2*IS
              T(2)=X
              T(3)=H
              DO 100 I=4,363
   100        T(I)=0.0
              DO 10 I=1,IS
              Y(2*I-1)=0.0
   10         Y(2*I)=0.0
              DO 11 I=1,I2S
   11         T(I+3)=Y(I)
              CALL COEFF(XX)
              XK=XX
              C1=-XK*SIN(T(2)*3.1415926)
              CALL INTS(T,I2S,K1,A2,A3,A4,A5,A6,A7)
   12         CALL COEFF(XX)
              XK=XX
              C1=-XK*SIN(T(2)*3.1415926)
              CALL INTM
              IF(ABS(T(2)-XMAX).GT.T(3)/2.)GO TO 12
              DO 14 I=1,IS
   14         V(I)=T(2*I+2)
C
C      CALCULATE W2(I)
C
              T(2)=X
              T(3)=H
              DO 200 I=4,363
   200        T(I)=0.0
              DO 20 I=1,IS
              Y(2*I-1)=0.0
   20         Y(2*I)=1.0
              DO 21 I=1,I2S
   21         T(I+3)=Y(I)
              C1=0.0
              CALL INTS(T,I2S,K1,A2,A3,A4,A5,A6,A7)
   22         CALL INTM
              IF(ABS(T(2)-XMAX).GT.T(3)/2.)GO TO 22
              DO 24 I=1,IS
   24         W2(I)=T(2*I+2)
              RETURN
              END
```

```
$IBFTC COEF
           SUBROUTINE COEFF(XX)
C
C      TO CALCULATE K(X), THE COEFFICIENT OF U SUB T.
C      CASE FOR IN HOMOGENEOUS MEDIUM,  K(X)= 1. + X
C
C      DIMENSION
C
C
           DIMENSION T(363),V(15),W2(15)
C
C      COMMON
C
           COMMON T,IS,K1,A2,A3,A4,A5,A6,A7,C1,X,H,XMAX,V,W2,XK
C
C      CALCULATE XX
C
           XX=1.+T(2)
           RETURN
           END
```

```
$IBFTC DAUX
              SUBROUTINE DAUX
C
C       DIMENSION
C
              DIMENSION T(363),V(15),W2(15)
C
C       COMMON
C
              COMMON T,IS,K1,A2,A3,A4,A5,A6,A7,C1,X,H,XMAX,V,W2,XK
              L=2*IS+2
              M=2*IS+3
              CALL COEFF(XX)
              XK=XX
              DO 1 I=1,IS
              S=I
              J=2*I+L
              K=2*I+M
              T(J)=T(2*I+3)
    1         T(K)=C1+S*XK*T(2*I+2)
              RETURN
              END
```

```
$IBFTC INPUT
              SUBROUTINE INPUT(N,R,W,T)
              DIMENSION R(15),W(15),T(15)
              DOUBLE PRECISION R,W,T
              READ(5,100)N
              DO 10  I=1,N
   10         READ(5,101)R(I)
              DO 11 I=1,N
   11         READ(5,101)W(I)
              DO 12 I=1,N
   12         T(I)=-DLOG(R(I))
  100         FORMAT(I12)
  101         FORMAT(D24.17)
              RETURN
              END
```

```
$IBFTC EXPINV
         SUBROUTINE EXPINV(N,R,W,A)
         DIMENSION R(15),W(15),A(15,15),C(17,17),B(15,15),P(15)
         DOUBLE PRECISION R,W,A,C,X1,X2,X,XI,B,PZERO,PREV2,PREV1,Z1,
      1Z2,Z3,PREV3,P,DENOM
C
C     LEGENDRE COEFFICIENTS
C
         NPLUS=N+1
         C(1,1)=1.0D0
         DO 20 M=1,NPLUS
         MP=M+1
         DO 15 N=MP,NPLUS
         X1=N+M-2
         X2=N-M
   15    C(N,M)=C(N-1,M)*X1/X2
         N=MP
         X=M
   20    C(N,N)=-C(N,N-1)*2.0D0/X
         DO 30 I=1,16
         DO 30 M=1,NPLUS
   30    C(I,M)=C(I+1,M)
         N=NPLUS-1
C
C      B COEFFICIENTS
C
         DO 100 I=1,N
         XI=R(I)
         K=N
         B(I,K)=C(N,N+1)
         DO 50 II=2,N
         K=K-1
   50    B(I,K)=C(N,K+1)+XI*B(I,K+1)
  100    CONTINUE
C
C      LEGENDRE DERIVATIVES
C
         NMINUS=N-1
         DO 180 I=1,N
         X=R(I)
         PZERO=1.0D0-2.0D0*X
         PREV2=PZERO
         PREV1=1.0D0
         DO 150 M=2,NMINUS
         Z1=M-1
         Z2=2*M-1
         Z3=M
         PREV3=-(Z1*PREV1-Z2*PZERO*PREV2)/Z3
         PREV1=PREV2
  150    PREV2=PREV3
         Z1=N
         Z2=2.0D0*X*(X-1.0D0)
  180    P(I)=PREV3*Z1/Z2
```

```
C
C      EXPLICIT INVERSE MATRIX
C
       DO 220 M=1,N
       DENOM=W(M)*P(M)
       DO 220 K=1,N
220    A(M,K)=B(M,K)/DENOM
       RETURN
       END
```

2. THE ROUTING PROBLEM

The following program is listed:

MAIN   program

The following subroutines are needed:

INPUT   subroutine

EXPINV   subroutine

```
$IBFTC MAIN
C
C      DIMENSION
C
            DIMENSION R(15),W(15),E(15,15),U(20,15),UTRANS(20,15),TIME(
         10,20),A(20,20),PROB(20,20,15),STO(20,15),F(20,15),T(15),NALT(20),
         2IALT(20,20),NEXT(20,15)
C
C      DOUBLE PRECISION
C
            DOUBLE PRECISION R,W,E,U,UTRANS,TIME,A,PROB,STO,F,T,S
C
C      INPUT
C
            READ(5,100)NUMBER,IAPRX
            DO 101 I=1,NUMBER
            READ(5,100)NALT(I)
            K=NALT(I)
  101       READ(5,100)(IALT(I,J),J=1,K)
            CALL INPUT(N,R,W,T)
            WRITE(6,104)NUMBER
            WRITE(6,105)
            DO 107 I=1,NUMBER
            K=NALT(I)
  107       WRITE(6,106)I,K,(IALT(I,J),J=1,K)
            WRITE(6,108)(T(I),I=1,N)
            CALL EXPINV(N,R,W,E)
            WRITE(6,115)
            DO 117 I=1,N
  117       WRITE(6,116)(E(I,J),J=1,N)
            DO 109 I=1,NUMBER
            READ(5,102)(TIME(I,J),J=1,NUMBER)
  109       READ(5,102)(A(I,J),J=1,NUMBER)
            WRITE(6,110)
            DO 111 I=1,NUMBER
            WRITE(6,112)(TIME(I,J),J=1,NUMBER)
            WRITE(6,112)(A(I,J),J=1,NUMBER)
  111       WRITE(6,113)
            DO 114 I=1,NUMBER
            DO 114 J=1,NUMBER
            DO 114 K=1,N
            S=K
  114       PROB(I,J,K)=(1.0D0/(2.0D0*A(I,J)*S))*(DEXP(-S*(TIME(I,J)-A(I
         1,J)  ))-DEXP(-S*(TIME(I,J)+A(I,J))))
C
C      INITIAL CONDITIONS
C
            DO 200 I=1,NUMBER
            DO 200 J=1,N
            U(I,J)=0.0D0
  2 0       NEXT(I,J)=NUMBER
            DO 201 J=1,N
  201       U(NUMBER,J)=1.0D0
```

```
           DO 203 I=1,NUMBER
           DO 203 J=1,N
           UTRANS(I,J)=0.0D0
           DO 203 K=1,N
  203      UTRANS(I,J)=UTRANS(I,J)+W(K)*R(K)**(J-1)*U(I,K)
           WRITE(6,500)
           DO 205 I=1,NUMBER
           WRITE(6,402)
  205      WRITE(6,403)I,(T(J),U(I,J),NEXT(I,J),J=1,N)
C
C          SUCCESSIVE APPROXIMATIONS
C
           DO 301 I=1,15
           DO 301 J=1,N
  301      U(I,J)=-1.0D+20
           DO 1000 IXX1=1,IAPRX
           DO 302 I=1,NUMBER
           K1=NALT(I)
           DO 302 J=1,K1
           J1=IALT(I,J)
           DO 304 IX1=1,N
  304      STO(I,IX1)=PROB(I,J1,IX1)*UTRANS(J1,IX1)
           DO 315 IX1=1,N
           F(J1,IX1)=0.0D0
           DO 315 IX2=1,N
  315      F(J1,IX1)=F(J1,IX1)+E(IX1,IX2)*STO(I,IX2)
           DO 306 IX1=1,N
           IF(U(I,IX1).GT.F(J1,IX1))GO TO 306
           U(I,IX1)=F(J1,IX1)
           NEXT(I,IX1)=J1
  306      CONTINUE
  302      CONTINUE
C
C          OUTPUT
C
           WRITE(6,400)IXX1
           DO 401 I=1,NUMBER
           WRITE(6,402)
  401      WRITE(6,403)I,(T(J),U(I,J),NEXT(I,J),J=1,N)
C
C          LAPLACE TRANSFORM OF U
C
           DO 404 I=1,NUMBER
           DO 404 J=1,N
           UTRANS(I,J)=0.0D0
           DO 404 K=1,N
  404      UTRANS(I,J)=UTRANS(I,J)+W(K)*R(K)**(J-1)*U(I,K)
 1000      CONTINUE
C
C          FORMATS
C
  100 FORMAT(6I12)
  102 FORMAT(6D12.8)
  104 FORMAT(1H14X16HNETWORK CONTAINS,I3,9H STATIONS)
  105 FORMAT(//5X65HSTATION          NO. OF ALTERNATIVES          ALTERNAT
```

```
      1IVE STATIONS ///)
106   FORMAT(7XI2,20XI2,26XI2/(57XI2))
108   FORMAT(//5X40HCALCULATIONS FOR TIME T= -LOG R          /(5X6D20.8)
110   FORMAT(//5X40HAVERAGE TIME AND MARGIN FROM I TO J
112   FORMAT(/(5X6D20.8))
113   FORMAT(//)
115   FORMAT(//5X16HEXPLICIT INVERSE//)
116   FORMAT(5X6D20.8)
400   FORMAT(//5X17HAPPROXIMATION NO.,I3)
402   FORMAT(//5X80HSTATION              TIME              PROBABILITY I TO
      1N      NEXT STATION                                        )
403   FORMAT(//I9,5X2D21.8,I15/(14X,2D21.8,I15))
500   FORMAT(//5X40HINITIAL APPROXIMATION
            CALL EXIT
            END
```

3. ADAPTIVE COMPUTATION

The following programs are listed:

SOLV	main program
TRANS	subroutine
QUAD	subroutine
PRQD	subroutine
INVERT	subroutine
INTERP	subroutine
SMOOTH	subroutine
TEST 1	subroutine
TEST 2	subroutine
MATRIX	subroutine
ODD	subroutine

The following subroutine is needed:

EXPINV	subroutine

```
$IBFTC SOLV
C TITLE        SOLV
C
C SUBROUTINES
C             TRANS
C             QUAD
C             PRQD
C             INVERT
C             INTERP
C             SMOOTH
C             TEST1
C             TEST2
C             MATRIX
C             ODD
C             EXPINV
C             FPTD
C
C     DIMENSION
C
              DIMENSION A(15,15),R(15),W(15),P(15),ROOT(15),WEIGHT(15),
     1        PHI(15),T(15),TIME(15),X(15),Y(15),Z(15),AS(15,15),B(15),
     2        C(15),D(15),ZTEMP(15),XLAM(20),SOL(20,15),LAMBDA(20)
C
C     DOUBLE PRECISION
C
              DOUBLE PRECISION A,R,W,P,ROOT,WEIGHT,PHI,T,TIME,X,Y
C
C     READ NUMBER OF QUADRATURES TO BE USED
C
    5         READ(5,78)NUM
C
C     OBTAIN LAPLACE TRANSFORM AND PRINT
C
              CALL TRANS(15,X)
              WRITE(6,79)(X(I),I=1,15)
C
C     READ IN AND PRINT THE VALUES OF XLAM AND EPS
C
              READ(5,78)LAM
              READ(5,81)(XLAM(I), I=1,LAM)
              READ(5,81)EPS
              WRITE(6,83)(XLAM(I),I=1,LAM)
              WRITE(6,84)EPS
C
C     READ AND PRINT ROOTS, WEIGHTS, AND DERIVATIVES
C
              CALL QUAD(N,R,W,P,T)
              WRITE(6,85)
              CALL PRQD(N,R,W,P,T)
C
C     CALCULATE AND PRINT THE EXPLICIT INVERSE
C
              CALL EXPINV(N,R,W,A)
              WRITE(6,87)
              DO 17 I=1,N
```

```
17          WRITE(6,88)(A(I,J),J=1,N)

C     INVERT TRANSFORM.  PRINT TRANSFOR AND MSD.

            CALL INVERT(N,A,X,Y)
            WRITE(6,89)  (Y(I),I=1,N)
            IF(NUM.EQ.0)GO TO 5

C     THIS IS AN INITIAL SOLUTION.  USING IT WE WILL FIND A SOLUTION AT
C     A NEW SET OF POINTS.  READ ROOTS, WEIGHTS, AND DERIVATIVES AT NEW
C     POINTS

            NO=0
22          NO=NO+1
            CALL QUAD(M,ROOT,WEIGHT,PHI,TIME)
            WRITE(6,91)
            CALL PRQD(M,ROOT,WEIGHT,PHI,TIME)

C     INTERPOLATE TO FIND FUNCTION AT NEW ROOTS

            CALL INTERP(N,R,Y,P,M,ROOT,Z)

C     NOW WE HAVE A SOLUTION AT M POINTS.  USING THIS AS AN INITIAL
C     APPROXIMATION, WE IMPROVE THESOLUTION USING THE LKB SMOOTHING
C     ROUTINE.  CALCULATE MATRIX A,  (AX=B).

            CALL MATRIX(M,ROOT,WEIGHT,AS)
            CALL TEST2(M,AS,Z,X,E)
            WRITE(6,92)E,(Z(I),I=1,M)
            WRITE(6,103)
            WRITE(6,94)
            DO 31 I=1,M
31          WRITE(6,95)(AS(I,J),J=1,M)

C     STORE INITIAL SOLUTION AND LAPLACE TRANSFORM BEFORE ENTERING
C     SMOOTHING ROUTINE

            DO 34 I=1,M
            C(I)=X(I)
34          ZTEMP(I)=Z(I)

C     DO SMOOTHING ROUTINE 20 TIMES FOR EACH LAMBDA.  RETAIN SOLUTIONS
C     FOR WHICH (X-C)**2 IS LESS THAN EPS.

            INDEX=0
            DO 56 I=1,LAM
            XL=XLAM(I)
            DO 58 K=1,20
            CALL SMOOTH(AS,C,Z,B,XL,M)
            DO 58 J=1,M
            Z(J)=B(J)
58          C(J)=X(J)
            CALL TEST1(M,ZTEMP,B,E)
            IF(E.GT.EPS) GO TO 59
            INDEX=INDEX+1
```

```
               LAMBDA(INDEX)=I
               DO 60 J=1,M
      60       SOL(INDEX,J)=B(J)
      59       DO 61 J=1,M
      61       Z(J)=ZTEMP(J)
      56       CONTINUE
C
C       FROM THE SOLUTIONS WHICH HAVE BEEN RETAINED SELECT THE ONE WITH
C       THE SMALLEST MSD.
C
               XMIN=1000000.
               DO 62 I=1,INDEX
               DO 63 J=1,M
      63       Z(J)=SOL(I,J)
               CALL TEST2(M,AS,Z,X,E)
               IF(E.GT.XMIN) GO TO 62
               XMIN=E
               K=I
      62       CONTINUE
C
C       PRINT SOLUTION, VALUE OF LAMBDA, AND THE MSD.
C
               L=LAMBDA(K)
               WRITE(6,99)XLAM(L),XMIN,(SOL(K,I), I=1,M)
C
C       DO WE REPEAT FOR NEW SET OF POINTS OR GO TO NEXT CASE
C
      69       IF(NO.EQ.NUM)GO TO 5
C
C       REPEAT PROCESS FOR NEW ROOTS
C
               N=M
               DO 76 I=1,N
               Y(I)=SOL(K,I)
               R(I)=ROOT(I)
               W(I)=WEIGHT(I)
               P(I)=PHI(I)
      76       T(I)=TIME(I)
               GO TO 22
C
C       FORMATS
C
      78       FORMAT(6I12)
      79       FORMAT(1H1,4X42HLAPLACE TRANSFORM OF EQUATION TO BE SOLVED
     1         /(5X6E20.8))
      81       FORMAT(6E12.8)
      82       FORMAT(E12.8)
      83       FORMAT(//5X30HVALUES OF LAMBDA                /(5X6E20.8))
      84       FORMAT(//5X33HDESIRED MEAN SQUARED DEVIATION - ,E16.8)
      85       FORMAT(///3X46HSOLUTION BY INVERSION OF THE LAPLACE TRANSFOR
     1M  )
      87       FORMAT(//5X16HEXPLICIT INVERSE/)
      88       FORMAT(5X6D20.8)
      89       FORMAT(//5X32HINVERSE LAPLACE TRANSFORM
     1         /(5X6D20.8))
```

```
91         FORMAT(///3X25HSOLUTION BY INTERPOLATION   )
92         FORMAT(//5X28HINTERPOLATED SOLUTION (MSD =E16.8,1H)
   1       /(5X6E20.8))
94         FORMAT(//5X10HMATRIX A   )
95         FORMAT(5X6E20.8)
99         FORMAT(//5X23HSOLUTION USING LAMBDA =E16.8,8H    MSD =E16.8/
   1(5X6E20.8))
103        FORMAT(///3X31HSOLUTION BY DYNAMIC PROGRAMMING)
           END
```

```
$IBFTC TRNS     LIST
C
C       SUBROUTINE TO READ IN THE LAPLACE TRANSFORM OF THE FUNCTION
C
        SUBROUTINE TRANS(N,T)
        DIMENSION T(15)
        DOUBLE PRECISION T
        DO 1 I=1,N
      1 READ(5,10)T(I)
     10 FORMAT(D24.16)
        RETURN
        END
```

```
$IBFTC QUAD      LIST
C
C TITLE      QUAD
C
C PURPOSE    TO READ IN DOUBLE PRECISION ROOTS, WEIGHTS, AND DERIVATIVES
C            AND TO CALCULATE TIME
C
C CALL       CALL QUAD(N,R,W,D,T)
C
       SUBROUTINE QUAD(N,R,W,D,T)
       DIMENSION R(15),W(15),D(15),T(15)
       DOUBLE PRECISION R,W,T,DLOG,D
       READ(5,10)N
       DO 20 I=1,N
    20 READ(5,11)R(I)
       DO 21 I=1,N
    21 READ(5,11)W(I)
       DO 22 I=1,N
    22 READ(5,11)D(I)
       DO 23 I=1,N
    23 T(I)=-DLOG(R(I))
    10 FORMAT(I12)
    11 FORMAT(D24.16)
       RETURN
       END
```

```
$IBFTC PRQD     LIST
C
C     SUBROUTINE TO PRINT ROOTS, WEIGHTS, DERIVATIVES AND TIMES
C
      SUBROUTINE PRQD(N,R,W,D,T)
      DIMENSION R(15),W(15),D(15),T(15)
      DOUBLE PRECISION R,W,D,T
      WRITE(6,10)N
      WRITE(6,11)(R(I),I=1,N)
      WRITE(6,12)(W(I),I=1,N)
      WRITE(6,13)(D(I),I=1,N)
      WRITE(6,14)(T(I),I=1,N)
   10 FORMAT(//5X12HDIMENSION = I2)
   11 FORMAT(//5X30HROOTS                           /(5X6D20.8))
   12 FORMAT(//5X30HWEIGHTS                         /(5X6D20.8))
   13 FORMAT(//5X30HDERIVATIVES                     /(5X6D20.8))
   14 FORMAT(//5X30HT = -LOG R                      /(5X6D20.8))
      RETURN
      END
```

```
$IBFTC IVRT    LIST
C TITLE        INVERT, INVERT LAPLACE TRANSFORM
C
C PURPOSE      GIVEN LAPLACE TRANSFORM, CALCULATE INVERSE
C
C CALL         CALL INVERT(N,A,B,C)
C
C
C INPUT        BY ARGUMENT IN CALL STATEMENT
C
C              SYMBOL              DEFINITION
C
C              N                   DIMENSION
C
C              A(15,15)            INVERSE MATRIX
C
C              B(15)               TRANSFORM
C
C
C OUTPUT       BY ARGUMENT IN CALL STATEMENT
C
C              SYMBOL              DEFINITION
C
C              C(15)               INVERSE
C
C METHOD       MULTIPLY EXPLICIT INVERSE MATRIX AND LAPLACE TRANSFORM
C
C NOTES        A, B, AND C ARE DOUBLE PRECISION
C
       SUBROUTINE INVERT(N,A,B,C)
C
C      DIMENSION
C
       DIMENSION A(15,15),B(15),C(15)
       DOUBLE PRECISION A,B,C
C
       DO 10 I=1,N
       C(I)=0.0
       DO 10 J=1,N
   10  C(I)=C(I)+A(I,J)*B(J)
       RETURN
       END
```

```
$IBFTC ITRP      LIST
C TITLE        ITRP,   'INTERPOLATION BY POLYNOMIAL APPROXIMATION'
C
C PURPOSE      TO FIND VALUES OF A FUNCTION AT POINTS OTHER THAN THOSE
C              WHICH ARE CALCULATED AUTOMATICALLY BY LAPLACE INVERSION
C              TECHNIQUES.
C
C CALL         INTERP(N,R,Y,PHI,M,ROOT,Z)
C
C
C INPUT        BY ARGUMENTS IN CALL STATEMENT
C
C              SYMBOL            DEFINITION
C
C              N                 NUMBER OF POINTS KNOWN (QUADRATURE SIZE O
C                                VALUES CALCULATED)
C
C              R(15)             ROOTS (POINTS WHERE VALUES OF THE FUNCTIO
C                                ARE KNOWN)
C
C              Y(15)             VALUES OF THE FUNCTIONS AT THE ROOTS
C
C              PHI(15)           DERIVATIVES OF THE SHIFTED LEGENDRE
C                                POLYNOMIALS EVALUATED AT THE ROOTS
C
C              M                 NUMBER OF NEW ROOTS AT WHICH VALUES OF TH
C                                FUNCTION ARE TO BE CALCULATED
C
C              ROOT(15)          ROOTS AT WHICH FUNCTIONS ARE TO BE
C                                CALCULATED
C
C OUTPUT       BY ARGUMENT IN CALL STATEMENT
C
C              SYMBOL            DEFINITION
C
C              Z(15)             VALUES OF THE FUNCTION EVALUATED AT ROOTS
C
C METHOD       POLYNOMIAL APPROXIMATION USING THE SHIFTED LEGENDRE
C              POLYNOMIALS AND THEIR DERIVATIVES
C
C SUBROUTINES USED
C
C              ODD(M,N,IODD)
C
C NOTES        VARIABLES CORRESPONDING TO R, Y, PHI, ROOT , AND Z MUST BE
C              DIMENSIONED R(15), Y(15), PHI(15), ROOT(15) , AND Z(15) IN
C              THE CALLING PROGRAM
C
      SUBROUTINE INTERP(N,R,Y,PHI,M,ROOT,Z)
C
C      DIMENSION
C
      DIMENSION    R(15),Y(15),PHI(15),ROOT(15),Z(15),P(3)
```

```
         TYPE

         DOUBLE PRECISION  R,Y,PHI,ROOT

         IF M AND N ARE BOTH ODD THERE WILL BE A ZERO DIVISOR AT ONE VALUE
         CHECK FOR THIS
               CALL ODD(N,M,IODD)
               IF(IODD.EQ.0) GO TO 10
               IODD=(M/2)+1
               N1=(N/2)+1

         CALCULATE Z(I) FOR EACH ROOT(I)

10             DO 11 I=1,M

         WILL THERE BE A ZERO DIVISOR

               IF(IODD.EQ.I) GO TO 14

         DIVISOR IS NOT ZERO.  FIND N-1 ORDER LEGENDRE POLYNOMIAL AT ROOT(I

               P(2)=1.0
               P(3)=1.-2.*SNGL(ROOT(I))
               DO 12 K=2,N
               XK=K
               P(1)=P(2)
               P(2)=P(3)
12             P(3)=((2.*XK-1.)*(1.-2.*SNGL(ROOT(I)))*P(2)-(XK-1.)*P(1))/XK

         CALCULATE FUNCTION AT ROOT(I)

               Z(I)=0.0
               DO 13 K=1,N
13             Z(I)=Z(I)+P(3)*SNGL(Y(K)/((ROOT(I)-R(K))*PHI(K)))
               GO TO 11

         DIVISOR IS ZERO.  SET Z(I)=Y(I)

14             Z(I)=SNGL(Y(N1))
11             CONTINUE
               RETURN
               END
```

```
$IBFTC SMTH
C TITLE          SMTH ,    'ILL-CONDITIONED LINEAR SYSTEMS'
C
C PURPOSE        TO FIND SOLUTION OF ILL-CONDITIONED LINEAR SYSTEMS VIA
C                DYNAMIC PROGRAMMING.
C
C CALL           SMOOTH(A,B,C,X,XLAM,N)
C
C INPUT          BY ARGUMENTS IN CALL STATEMENT
C
C                SYMBOL                   DEFINITION
C
C                A(15,15)           MATRIX INPUT BY CALLING PROGRAM AX=B.
C
C                B(15)              OBSERVATION VECTOR B FROM CALLING
C                                   PROGRAM
C
C                C(15)              INITIAL APPROXIMATION TO SOLUTION
C                                   VECTOR X.
C
C                N                  DIMENSION OF LINEAR SYSTEM
C
C                XLAM               WEIGHTING VALUE ON INITIAL APPROX.
C
C OUTPUT         BY ARGUMENT IN CALL STATEMENT
C
C                SYMBOL                   DEFINITION
C
C                X(15)              SOLUTION VECTOR X OF THE SYSTEM
C
C METHOD         SOLUTION TO AN ILL-CONDITIONED LINEAR SYSTEM, AX=B, IS
C                FOUND BY INTRODUCING AN INITIAL APPROXIMATION C.
C                A DYNAMIC PROGRAMMING SOLUTION OF
C                    MIN((AX-B,AX-B)+XLAM(X-C,X-C))  ,
C                    X
C
C                YIELDS THE SOLUTION VECTOR X.
C
C NOTES          VARIABLES CORRESPONDING TO A, B, C, AND X MUST BE
C                DIMENSIONED A(15,15),B(15),C(15),AND X(15) IN THE
C                CALLING PROGRAM.
C
C                THE PROGRAM IS WRITTEN IN  FORTRAN IV
C                EXECUTES ON 7044 UNDER IBSYS
C
C
C
       SUBROUTINE SMOOTH(A,B,C,X,XLAM,N)
C
C      DIMENSION
C
          DIMENSION A(15,15),B(15),C(15),X(15),XIDENT(15,15),XK(15),AK
     1RN(15,15),Q(15,15),P(15),ALPHA(15,15),RHO(15)
```

```
C
C
C        FORM IDENTITY MATRIX
C
             DO 100 I=1,N
             DO 101 J=1,N
    101      XIDENT(I,J)=0.0
    100      XIDENT(I,I)=1.0
C
C        FORM KRONECKER CROSSPRODUCT
C
             XK(1)=0.
             DO 102 I=1,N
    102      XK(1)=XK(1)+A(I,1)**2
             DO 103 I=1,N
             DO 103 J=1,N
    103      AKRN(I,J)=(A(I,1)*A(J,1))/(XLAM       +XK(1))
C
C        FORM Q(1),  Q1=I-AKRN
C
             DO 104 I=1,N
             DO 104 J=1,N
    104      Q(I,J)=XIDENT(I,J)-AKRN(I,J)
C
C        FORM VECTOR P(1)
C
             DO 105 I=1,N
    105      P(I)=(-XLAM*C(1)*A(I,1))/(XLAM+XK(1))
C
C        FORM R(1)
C
             R=XLAM*(C(1)**2)-((XLAM*C(1))**2)/(XLAM+XK(1))
C
C        DETERMINE ALPHA(1) AND RHO(1)
C
             DO 106 I=1,N
    106      ALPHA(I,1)=A(I,1)
             RHO(1)=0.0
C
C            ITERATION OF RECURRENCE RELATIONSHIPS
C
C        DETERMINE ALPHA(STORE COLUMNWISE), RHO, AND XK
C
             DO 107 IXX1=2,N
             DO 108 I=1,N
             ALPHA(I,IXX1)=0.
             DO 108 J=1,N
    108      ALPHA(I,IXX1)=ALPHA(I,IXX1)+Q(I,J)*A(J,IXX1)
C
C
             RHO(IXX1)=0.0
             DO 109 I=1,N
    109      RHO(IXX1)=RHO(IXX1)+P(I)*A(I,IXX1)
C
C
             XK(IXX1)=0.0
```

```
              DO 110 I=1,N
   110        XK(IXX1)=XK(IXX1)+(ALPHA(I,IXX1)*A(I,IXX1))
C
C       FORM KRONECKER CROSSPRODUCT OF ALPHA
C
              DO 111 I=1,N
              DO 111 J=1,N
   111        AKRN(I,J)= (ALPHA(I,IXX1)*ALPHA(J,IXX1))/(XLAM+XK(IXX1))
C
C       CALCULATE NEW Q
C
              DO 112 I=1,N
              DO 112 J=1,N
   112        Q(I,J)=Q(I,J)-AKRN(I,J)
C
C       CALCULATE NEW P
C
              DO 113 I=1,N
   113        P(I)=P(I)-((XLAM*C(IXX1)+RHO(IXX1))*ALPHA(I,IXX1))/(XLAM+XK(
     1IXX1))
C
C       CALCULATE NEW R
C
              R=R+XLAM*C(IXX1)**2-((XLAM*C(IXX1)+RHO(IXX1))**2)/(XLAM+XK(I
     1XX1))
   107 CONTINUE
C
C       CALCULATE X(N), X(N-1), . . . , X(1)
C
              DO 114 IXX2=1,N
              IXX3=N+1-IXX2
              X(IXX3)=(XLAM*C(IXX3)+RHO(IXX3))/(XLAM+XK(IXX3))
              DO 115 I=1,N
   115        X(IXX3)=X(IXX3)+(ALPHA(I,IXX3)*B(I))/(XLAM+XK(IXX3))
C
C       CALCULATE NEW VALUES OF B
C
              DO 116 I=1,N
   116        B(I)=B(I)-X(IXX3)*A(I,IXX3)
   114        CONTINUE
C
C
              RETURN
              END
```

```
$IBFTC TST1
          SUBROUTINE TEST1(N,C,X,E)
          DIMENSION C(15),X(15)
          E=0.0
          DO 1 I=1,N
    1     E=E+(X(I)-C(I))**2
          RETURN
          END
```

```
$IBFTC TST2
        SUBROUTINE TEST2(N,A,X,B,E)
        DIMENSION A(15,15),X(15),B(15),C(15)
        DOUBLE PRECISION B
        E=0.0
        DO 1 I=1,N
        C(I)=-B(I)
        DO 1 J=1,N
   1    C(I)=C(I)+A(I,J)*X(J)
        DO 2 I=1,N
   2    E=E+C(I)**2
        RETURN
        END
```

```
$IBFTC MTRX     LIST
C TITLE     MATRIX
C
C CALL      CALL MATRIX(N,R,W,A)
C
C PURPOSE   TO FORM 'A' MATRIX OF AX=B
C
C METHOD    A(I,J)= W(J)*R(J)**(I-1)
C
           SUBROUTINE MATRIX(N,R,W,A)
           DIMENSION A(15,15),R(15),W(15)
           DOUBLE PRECISION R,W
           DO 11 J=1,N
    11     A(1,J)=W(J)
           DO 10 I=2,N
    10     A(I,J)=W(J)*R(J)**(I-1)
           RETURN
           END
```

```
$IBFTC ODD        LIST
       SUBROUTINE ODD(N,M,IODD)
C
C      TO DETERMINE IF BOTH M AND N ARE ODD
C
            NODD=N
C
C      IS N ODD
C
   12       IF(NODD.EQ.1)GO TO 10
            IF(NODD.EQ.0)GO TO 11
            NODD=NODD-2
            GO TO 12
C
C      N IS ODD.  IS M ODD
C
   10       NODD = M
   13       IF(NODD.EQ.1)GO TO 14
            IF(NODD.EQ.0)GO TO 11
            NODD=NODD-2
            GO TO 13
C
C      N AND M ARE BOTH ODD
C
   14       IODD=1
            RETURN
C
C      BOTH ARE NOT ODD
C
   11       IODD=0
            RETURN
            END
```

Appendix Two

ROOTS OF THE SHIFTED LEGENDRE POLYNOMIALS AND CORRESPONDING WEIGHTS

The roots, x_i, of the shifted Legendre polynomial P_N^* are obtained from the roots of the Legendre polynomial r_i by the formula

$$x_i = \frac{1 + r_i}{2}.$$

The weights in interval $(0,1)$ are then

$$w_i = \frac{a_i}{2},$$

where a_i are Christoffel weights for the interval $(-1,1)$. The roots r_i and the weights a_i were obtained from Gawlick.* The entries in the tables were computed with sixteen figures of accuracy and are printed to seventeen digits, although only the first fifteen are believed to be accurate.

Checks: The quantities r_i and w_i obtained by the inverse relations

$$r_i = 2(x_i - 1)$$

$$a_i = 2w_i$$

agreed with the original data to sixteen figures.

* Gawlick, H. J., *Zeros of Legendre Polynomials of Orders 2-64 and Weight Coefficients of Gauss Quadrature Formulae*, Armament Research and Development Establishment, ARDE Memorandum (B) 77/58, December 1958.

ROOTS OF THE SHIFTED LEGENDRE POLYNOMIALS AND CORRESPONDING WEIGHTS

ROOTS	WEIGHTS

$N = 3$

ROOTS	WEIGHTS
1.1270166537925834E −1	2.7777777777777767E −1
5.0000000000000000E −1	4.4444444444444428E −1
8.8729833462074160E −1	2.7777777777777767E −1

$N = 4$

ROOTS	WEIGHTS
6.9431844202973879E −2	1.7392742256872686E −1
3.3000947820757191E −1	3.2607257743127297E −1
6.6999052179242805E −1	3.2607257743127297E −1
9.3056815579702609E −1	1.7392742256872686E −1

$N = 5$

ROOTS	WEIGHTS
4.6910077030668073E −2	1.1846344252809450E −1
2.3076534494715854E −1	2.3931433524968315E −1
5.0000000000000000E −1	2.8444444444444437E −1
7.6923465505284136E −1	2.3931433524968315E −1
9.5308992296933192E −1	1.1846344252809450E −1

$N = 6$

ROOTS	WEIGHTS
3.3765242898424085E −2	8.5662246189585146E −2
1.6939530676686780E −1	1.8038078652406926E −1
3.8069040695840160E −1	2.3395696728634547E −1
6.1930959304159838E −1	2.3395696728634547E −1
8.3060469323313217E −1	1.8038078652406926E −1
9.6623475710157577E −1	8.5662246189585146E −2

$N = 7$

ROOTS	WEIGHTS
2.5446043828620866E −2	6.4742483084434816E −2
1.2923440720030282E −1	1.3985269574463828E −1
2.9707742431130145E −1	1.9091502525255938E −1
5.0000000000000000E −1	2.0897959183673466E −1
7.0292257568869853E −1	1.9091502525255938E −1
8.7076559279969706E −1	1.3985269574463828E −1
9.7455395617137909E −1	6.4742483084434816E −2

ROOTS AND WEIGHTS (continued)

ROOTS   WEIGHTS

N = 8

ROOTS	WEIGHTS
1.9855071751231967E −2	5.0614268145188114E −2
1.0166676129318669E −1	1.1119051722668717E −1
2.3723379504183554E −1	1.5685332293894362E −1
4.0828267875217507E −1	1.8134189168918094E −1
5.9171732124782482E −1	1.8134199168918094E −1
7.6276620495816439E −1	1.5685332293894362E −1
8.9833323870681328E −1	1.1119051722668717E −1
9.8014492824876801E −1	5.0614268145188114E −2

N = 9

ROOTS	WEIGHTS
1.5919880246187067E −2	4.0637194180787190E −2
8.1984446336682168E −2	9.0324080347428683E −2
1.9331428364970484E −1	1.3030534820146768E −1
3.3787328829809553E −1	1.5617353852000137E −1
5.0000000000000000E −1	1.6511967750062983E −1
6.6212671170190437E −1	1.5617353852000137E −1
8.0668571635029504E −1	1.3030534820146768E −1
9.1801555366331779E −1	9.0324080347428683E −2
9.8408011975381288E −1	4.0637194180787190E −2

N = 10

ROOTS	WEIGHTS
1.3046735741414350E −2	3.3335672154344053E −2
6.7468316655507897E −2	7.4725674575290263E −2
1.6029521585048788E −1	1.0954318125799097E −1
2.8330230293537641E −1	1.3463335965499813E −1
4.2556283050918439E −1	1.4776211235737637E −1
5.7443716949081551E −1	1.4776211235737637E −1
7.1669769706462353E −1	1.3463335965499813E −1
8.3970478414951203E −1	1.0954318125799097E −1
9.3253168334449210E −1	7.4725674575290263E −2
9.8695326425858560E −1	3.3335672154344053E −2

N = 11

ROOTS	WEIGHTS
1.0885670926971624E −2	2.7834283558086820E −2
5.6468700115952450E −2	6.2790184732452276E −2
1.3492399721297543E −1	9.3145105463867085E −2
2.4045193539659415E −1	1.1659688229599520E −1
3.6522842202382754E −1	1.3140227225512328E −1
5.0000000000000000E −1	1.3646254338895027E −1
6.3477157797617236E −1	1.3140227225512328E −1
7.5954806460340584E −1	1.1659688229599520E −1
8.6507600278702456E −1	9.3145105463867085E −2
9.4353129988404748E −1	6.2790184732452276E −2
9.8911432907302829E −1	2.7834283558086820E −2

ROOTS AND WEIGHTS (continued)

ROOTS   WEIGHTS

N = 12

ROOTS	WEIGHTS
9.2196828766404337E −3	2.3587668193255901E −2
4.7941371814762656E −2	5.3469662997659206E −2
1.1504866290284776E −1	8.0039164271673080E −2
2.0634102285669131E −1	1.0158371336153293E −1
3.1608425050090991E −1	1.1674626826917738E −1
4.3738329574426550E −1	1.2457352290670135E −1
5.6261670425573439E −1	1.2457352290670135E −1
6.8391574949909003E −1	1.1674626826917738E −1
7.9365897714330867E −1	1.0158371336153293E −1
8.8495133709715219E −1	8.0039164271673080E −2
9.5205862818523723E −1	5.3469662997659206E −2
9.9078031712335956E −1	2.3587668193255901E −2

N = 13

ROOTS	WEIGHTS
7.9084726407059874E −3	2.0242002382657933E −2
4.1200800388511149E −2	4.6060749918864205E −2
9.9210954633345167E −2	6.9436755109893594E −2
1.7882533027982994E −1	8.9072990380972853E −2
2.7575362448177664E −1	1.0390802376844421E −1
3.8477084202243260E −1	1.1314159013144858E −1
5.0000000000000000E −1	1.1627577661543691E −1
6.1522915797756727E −1	1.1314159013144858E −1
7.2424637551822334E −1	1.0390802376844421E −1
8.2117466972017005E −1	8.9072990380972853E −2
9.0078904536665476E −1	6.9436755109893594E −2
9.5879919961148880E −1	4.6060749918864205E −2
9.9209152735929392E −1	2.0242002382657933E −2

N = 14

ROOTS	WEIGHTS
6.8580956515939534E −3	1.7559730165875926E −2
3.5782558162134O7E −2	4.0079043579880089E −2
8.6399342465117711E −2	6.0759285343951576E −2
1.5635354759415735E −1	7.8601583579096727E −2
2.4237568182092299E −1	9.2769198738968867E −2
3.4044381553605518E −1	1.0259923186064778E −1
4.4597252564632814E −1	1.0763192673157886E −1
5.5402747435367176E −1	1.0763192673157886E −1
6.5955618446394480E −1	1.0259923186064778E −1
7.5762431817907698E −1	9.2769198738968867E −2
8.4364645240584259E −1	7.8601583579096727E −2
9.1360065753488228E −1	6.0759285343951576E −2
9.6421744183178654E −1	4.0079043579880089E −2
9.9314190434840589E −1	1.7559730165875926E −2

ROOTS AND WEIGHTS (continued)

ROOTS	WEIGHTS
	N = 15

ROOTS	WEIGHTS
6.0037409897574223E −3	1.5376620998058628E −2
3.1363303799647246E −2	3.5183023744054046E −2
7.5896708294786505E −2	5.3579610233585954E −2
1.3779113431991500E −1	6.9785338963077129E −2
2.1451391369573062E −1	8.3134602908496945E −2
3.0292432646121834E −1	9.3080500007781079E −2
3.9940295300128272E −1	9.9215742663555754E −2
5.0000000000000000E −1	1.0128912096278060E −1
6.0059704699871723E −1	9.9215742663555754E −2
6.9707567353878161E −1	9.3080500007781079E −2
7.8548608630426927E −1	8.3134602908496945E −2
8.6220886568008490E −1	6.9785338963077129E −2
9.2410329170521343E −1	5.3579610233585954E −2
9.6863669620035270E −1	3.5183023744054046E −2
9.9399625901024251E −1	1.5376620998058628E −2

Appendix Three

COEFFICIENTS OF THE POLYNOMIALS $P_N^*(x)/(x - x_i)$ IN ORDER OF SMALLEST TO LARGEST ROOT x_i AND LOWEST TO HIGHEST POWER

These are the coefficients of the polynomials

$$\frac{P_N^*(x)}{x - x_i} = \sum_{k=0}^{N-1} b_{ik} x^k,$$

where x_i is a root of the polynomial $P_N^*(x)$. They were found by synthetic division:

$$b_{i,N-1} = c_{NN}$$

$$b_{i,N-2} = c_{N,N-1} + x_i b_{i,N-1}$$

.

.

.

$$b_{i,k-1} = c_{Nk} + x_i b_{ik}$$

.

.

.

$$b_{i0} = c_{N1} + x_i b_{i1}.$$

$$\text{Remainder} = c_{N0} + x_i b_{i0},$$

for $i = 1, 2, \ldots, N$. The numbers c_{Nm} are coefficients in the expansion of

$$P_N^*(x) = \sum_{m=0}^{N} c_{Nm} x^m.$$

Checks: (1) Hand calculations were made for low values of N and agreed with those computed by machine.

(2) Because x_i is a root of the polynomial $P_N^*(x)$, there should be no remainder term. Indeed the remainder computed by the above formula was of the order of 10^{-16}, extremely close to zero.

COEFFICIENTS OF THE POLYNOMIALS $P_N^*(x)/(x - x_i)$ IN ORDER OF SMALLEST
TO LARGEST ROOT, x_i, AND LOWEST TO HIGHEST POWER

For example, $P_3^*(x)/(x - 0.1127) = - 8.87x^0 + 27.7x^1 - 20x^2$

N = 3

I = 1   -8.8729833462074160E   0
           2.7745966692414825E   1
           -1.9999999999999998E   1

I = 2   -2.0000000000000000E   0
           1.9999999999999998E   1
           -1.9999999999999998E   1

I = 3   -1.1270166537925838E   0
           1.2254033307585165E   1
           -1.9959999999999998E   1

N = 4

I = 1   -1.4402613260230381E   1
           8.0616996480843461E   1
           -1.3513977090579176E   2
           6.9999999999999995E   1

I = 2   -3.0302159969205888E   0
           5.1422110950418300E   1
           -1.1689933652546993E   2
           6.9999999999999995E   1

I = 3   -1.4925584280277455E   0
           2.7623437899478380E   1
           -9.3100663474530023E   1
           6.9999999999999995E   1

I = 4   -1.0746123148212660E   0
           2.0337454669259824E   1
           -7.4860229094208161E   1
           6.9999999999999995E   1

N = 5

I = 1   -2.1317381323979449E   1
           1.8509069320743542E   2
           -5.3100119141308876E   2
           6.1817866058827135E   2
           -2.5199999999999995E   2

I = 2   -4.3334063016653683E   0
           1.1122377887464798E   2
           -4.2803749907929242E   2
           5.7184713307331582E   2
           -2.5199999999999995E   2

I = 3   -2.0000000000000000E   0
           5.5999999999999996E   1
           -3.0799999999999996E   2
           5.0399999999999991E   2
           -2.5199999999999995E   2

I = 4   -1.2999934329939079E   0
           3.7309820063988911E   1
           -2.2449609985934446E   2
           4.3615286692668382E   2
           -2.5199999999999995E   2

I = 5   -1.0492189413613850E   0
           3.0375707853927420E   1
           -1.8846520964827403E   2
           3.8982133941172820E   2
           -2.5199999999999995E   2

COEFFICIENTS OF THE POLYNOMIALS $P_N^*(x)/(x - x_i)$ (continued)

N = 6   N = 7

I = 1   -2.9616253702314531E   1   I = 1   -3.9298839801385403E   1
           3.6676017213735025E   2   6.5633621914262665E   2
          -1.5767642490477813E   3   -3.9166709579142730E   3
           3.0574561913498299E   3   1.1134502636006826E   4
          -2.7408009155618552E   3   -1.6328564345465488E   4
           9.2399999999999993E   2   1.1924669177580167E   4
                                                     -3.4319999999999994E   3

I = 2   -5.9033512739302693E   0
           2.1309119724165759E   2   I = 2   -7.7378774094586120E   0
          -1.2214553443508497E   3   3.7344638812587279E   2
           2.7069501770803299E   3   -2.9601529512276085E   3
          -2.6154787365474132E   3   9.5937844698798108E   3
           9.2399999999999993E   2   -1.5136955958549106E   4
                                                     1.1568467514488558E   4
I = 3   -2.6268064067851923E   0   -3.4319999999999994E   3
           1.0342575718625122E   2
          -8.3157924924633324E   2   I = 3   -3.3661258586653417E   0
           2.2286370637292520E   3   1.7717224478888935E   2
          -2.4202420639704360E   3   -1.9484070745293945E   3
           9.2399999999999993E   2   7.5791451696147883E   3
                                                    -1.3366397125566265E   4
I = 4   -1.6147012919478882E   0   1.0992430279763609E   4
           6.5210193999593783E   1   -3.4319999999999994E   3
          -5.7287955811880237E   2
           1.7876688078475044E   3   I = 4   -1.9999999999997726E   0
          -2.1957579360295626E   3   1.0800000000000042E   2
           9.2399999999999993E   2   -1.2959999999999984E   3
                                                     5.8079999999999989E   3
I = 5   -1.2039421497940310E   0   -1.1483999999999998E   4
           4.9116093591293283E   1   1.0295999999999998E   4
          -4.4652276760565791E   2   -3.4319999999999994E   3
           1.4850352308906739E   3
          -2.0045212634525850E   3   I = 5   -1.4226317870352857E   0
           9.2399999999999993E   2   7.7643498872534770E   1
                                                    -9.6505152144649155E   2
                                                     4.6021405350141435E   3
I = 6   -1.0349451752281382E   0   -9.8842457267481975E   3
           4.2396585843853458E   1   9.5995697202363831E   3
          -3.9079883163057313E   2   -3.4319999999999994E   3
           1.3342525291024056E   3
          -1.8791990844381433E   3
           9.2399999999999993E   2   I = 6   -1.1484146919304478E   0
                                                     6.2992366443545386E   1
                                                    -7.9586014799722057E   2
                                                     3.9093642194310200E   3
                                                    -8.7746183861063026E   3
                                                     9.0235324855114367E   3
                                                    -3.4319999999999994E   3

COEFFICIENTS OF THE POLYNOMIALS $P_N^*(x)/(x - x_i)$ (continued)

(N = 7)   (N = 8)

I = 7   -1.0261104515220438E 0   I = 5   -1.6899961587901941E 0
         5.6409282626533796E 1   1.1882363641635285E 2
        -7.1785734688499935E 2   -1.9285836709615197E 3
         3.5730629700533994E 3   1.2356265511410111E 4
        -8.1862184575646234E 3   -3.7676325650863881E 4
         8.6673308224198243E 3   5.8128557529128688E 4
        -3.4319999999999994E 3   -4.3864598075540479E 4
                                              1.2869999999999999E 4

            N = 8   I = 6   -1.3110177056852805E 0
                                              9.2674507384856923E 1
                                             -1.5303843891185073E 3
I = 1   -5.0364965311090079E 1   1.0107442569908218E 4
         1.0896477716111751E 3   -3.2175727333695740E 4
        -8.5797840734700017E 3   5.2304719856449919E 4
         3.3251752237512190E 4   -4.1663198942188417E 4
        -7.0422700054007218E 4   1.2869999999999999E 4
         8.3066934567508105E 4
        -5.1224465226561628E 4
         1.2869999999999999E 4   I = 7   -1.1131726589945998E 0
                                              7.8909278079312565E 1
                                             -1.3147578994415418E 3
I = 2   -9.8360564188348149E 0   8.8221628223031771E 3
         6.1144805628160749E 2   -2.8750842187334652E 4
        -6.3791935089591120E 3   4.8223928433314879E 4
         2.8139054049247076E 4   -3.9918451217843306E 4
        -6.4042031711590041E 4   1.2869999999999999E 4
         7.8983221126254984E 4
        -5.0171548782156669E 4
         1.2869999999999999E 4   I = 8   -1.0202572815223760E 0
                                              7.2417599349616228E 1
                                             -1.2116395916798197E 3
I = 3   -4.2152510346327431E 0   8.1909931653316867E 3
         2.8572973320859941E 2   -2.6994994385108745E 4
        -4.1067937501045763E 3   4.5990143208138265E 4
         2.1637752955856019E 4   -3.8865534773438347E 4
        -5.4849887815727527E 4   1.2869999999999999E 4
         7.2595526203319362E 4
        -4.8426801057811568E 4
         1.2869999999999999E 4   N = 9

I = 4   -2.4492834304311656E 0   I = 1   -6.2814542856847923E 1
         1.7034941766850133E 2   1.7076420628015202E 3
        -2.6688631162648687E 3   -1.7108039318556499E 4
         1.6094576688431505E 4   8.6179083022441762E 4
        -4.5447490861672114E 4   -2.4566246209640416E 5
         6.5210969075885714E 4   4.1391881105224017E 5
        -4.6225401924459496E 4   -4.0836921177951919E 5
         1.2869999999999999E 4   2.1801597542243031E 5
                                             -4.8619999999999991E 4

COEFFICIENTS OF THE POLYNOMIALS $P_N^*(x)/(x - x_i)$ (continued)

(N = 9)   (N = 9)

I = 2

-1.2197435546412489E 1
9.4899176526824219E 2
-1.2575656490961200E 4
7.2017849395379975E 4
-2.2043389218491333E 5
3.8809931928332471E 5
-3.9422941985782510E 5
2.1480391621911047E 5
-4.8619999999999991E 4

I = 3

-5.1729234959791199E 0
4.3880397714289820E 2
-7.9724891185476244E 3
5.4354549922924979E 4
-1.8485674934310307E 5
3.4863047564048849E 5
-3.7136171732450801E 5
2.0939105952895131E 5
-4.8619999999999991E 4

I = 4

-2.9596894298353929E 0
2.5761228716420911E 2
-5.0977327077604872E 3
3.9607355052089001E 4
-1.4941295064252504E 5
3.0437164735776058E 5
-3.4346708266518346E 5
2.0236260072294656E 5
-4.8619999999999991E 4

I = 5

-1.9999999999977262E 0
1.7600000000000450E 2
-3.6079999999999898E 3
2.9743999999999996E 4
-1.2069199999999999E 5
2.6311999999999999E 5
-3.1459999999999998E 5
1.9447999999999999E 5
-4.8619999999999991E 4

I = 6

-1.5102849383971630E 0
1.3364468386142036E 2
-2.7885226249108425E 3
2.3698601940943281E 4
-1.0026992852834299E 5
2.2953623345146167E 5
-2.8828887760455730E 5
1.8659739927705339E 5
-4.8619999999999991E 4

I = 7

-1.2396401470080178E 0
1.1003090553601506E 2
-2.3180887631484594E 3
2.0034954021466004E 4
-8.6843047494984144E 4
2.0504757819858143E 5
-2.6698430062184863E 5
1.7956894047104862E 5
-4.8619999999999991E 4

I = 8

-1.0893061626507858E 0
9.6850966721155575E 1
-2.0513258471103084E 3
1.7895855998660885E 4
-7.8641525966798919E 4
1.8911495926230539E 5
-2.5196200632405156E 5
1.7415608378088943E 5
-4.8619999999999991E 4

I = 9

-1.0161774228623841E 0
9.0423351504548907E 1
-1.9201451290045014E 3
1.6827750646094001E 4
-7.4447443742928154E 4
1.8068097575383711E 5
-2.4361738382250654E 5
1.7094402457756958E 5
-4.8619999999999991E 4

N = 10

I = 1

-7.6647524700427744E 1
2.5563846743443433E 3
-3.1702590889667017E 4
2.0061792943536711E 5
-7.3520846553093441E 5
1.6515651804509900E 6
-2.3082263752316074E 6
1.9570891351267699E 6
-9.2136953729135910E 5
1.8475599999999998E 5

COEFFICIENTS OF THE POLYNOMIALS $P_N^*(x)/(x - x_i)$ (continued)

(N = 10)   (N = 10)

I = 2			I = 6		
-1.4821771900816398E	1		-1.7408344255939596E	0
1.4107099868099871E	3		1.8846128231981848E	2
-2.3111440902723589E	4		-4.8421983559067970E	3
1.6613070627665275E	5		5.1315971893362108E	4
-6.5333323711654687E	5		-2.7660819415199488E	5
1.5329086008107752E	6		8.3585782980166624E	5
-2.2050557441480069E	6		-1.4724363518260410E	6
1.9076251229025594E	6		1.4994218583338558E	6
-9.1131482368799474E	5		-8.1764928631355466E	5
1.8475599999999998E	5		1.8475599999999998E	5

I = 3			I = 7		
-6.2384893690939264E	0		-1.3952884236350371E	0
6.4731508099210834E	2		1.5153489682076126E	2
-1.4490045174987182E	4		-3.9325717310419951E	3
1.2370896236546930E	5		4.2399226889406316E	4
-5.3963580369867525E	5		-2.3414442909178547E	5
1.3545020364415553E	6		7.2919387497500398E	5
-2.0410962474613905E	6		-1.3289928639733181E	6
1.8257797089314597E	6		1.4019399534028122E	6
-8.9416449710032708E	5		-7.9136580028112834E	5
1.8475599999999998E	5		1.8475599999999998E	5

I = 4			I = 8		
-3.5297983448708123E	0		-1.1908947273492742E	0
3.7581834158056919E	2		1.2958018976021090E	2
-9.1569381241887910E	3		-3.3826409755622437E	3
8.8205341611175110E	4		3.6843137741286504E	4
-4.2848033560290117E	5		-2.0646168216643743E	5
1.1587468968509622E	6		6.5534260161554693E	5
-1.8458484019747726E	6		-1.2222597962496666E	6
1.7222295511537849E	6		1.3236797321288418E	6
-8.7143819971887132E	5		-7.6863950289967259E	5
1.8475599999999998E	5		1.8475599999999998E	5

I = 5			I = 9		
-2.3498292809112371E	0		-1.0723496239962884E	0
2.5295952325132740E	2		1.1680852492361277E	2
-6.3845812696981596E	3		-3.0596188054903570E	3
6.5643464907114141E	4		3.3522058019943461E	4
-3.3970667720184231E	5		-1.8947124814716368E	5
9.7999471029732453E	5		6.0832759034876904E	5
-1.6488406397314147E	6		-1.1510090529060528E	6
1.6094435678254168E	6		1.2683225333986001E	6
-8.4515471368644501E	5		-7.5148917631200492E	5
1.8475599999999998E	5		1.8475599999999998E	5

COEFFICIENTS OF THE POLYNOMIALS $P_N^*(x)/(x - x_i)$ (continued)

(N = 10)   (N = 11)

I = 10   −1.0132192032462370E   0   I = 4   −4.1588353129682218E   0
           1.1042749919736705E   2   5.3167035015199352E   2
          −2.8973737707334974E   3   −1.5630274065580427E   4
           3.1838008310222907E   4   1.8477591316176545E   5
          −1.8072992729171714E   5   −1.1048947740846406E   6
           5.8364067840740396E   5   3.7975207993617691E   6
          −1.1125545264977261E   6   −7.9857589728738308E   6
           1.2373488367958963E   6   1.0464299332738111E   7
          −7.4143446270864057E   5   −8.3456623626341172E   6
           1.8475599999999998E   5   3.7102535103093092E   6
                                                −7.0543199999999996E   5

                    N = 11   I = 5   −2.7380125414510416E   0
                                                   3.5392094279594665E   2
                                                  −1.0777033822814762E   4
I = 1   −9.1863882962168990E   1   1.3493737947363241E   5
           3.6870595581191975E   3   −8.6387751199106688E   5
          −5.5388450186095940E   4   3.1604565475536603E   6
           4.2914670535641570E   5   −7.0029225301624418E   6
          −1.9570033658468077E   6   9.58C2989549627159E   6
           5.6048574830623633E   6   −7.9148578553086696E   6
          −1.0367254135710969E   7   3.6222321837948867E   6
           1.2370929196046653E   7   −7.0543199999999996E   5
          −9.1956485387888351E   6
           3.8721968993866439E   6   I = 6   −1.9999999999581632E   0
          −7.0543199999999996E   5   2.6000000000008362E   2
                                                  −8.0599999999998299E   3
                                                   1.0400000000000021E   5
I = 2   −1.7708925439165323E   1   −6.9289999999999939E   5
           2.0239721177599290E   3   2.65C2319999999996E   6
          −4.0128918809659568E   4   −6.1349599999999995E   6
           3.5295803072169213E   5   8.7339199999999994E   6
          −1.7264780148669691E   6   −7.4742199999999993E   6
           5.1628244414053803E   6   3.5271599999999995E   6
          −9.8264624022726944E   6   −7.0543199999999996E   5
           1.1961628235470691E   7
          −9.0209578666288177E   6   I = 7   −1.5753698410456422E   0
           3.84C0411719398026E   6   2.0546702890319092E   2
          −7.0543199999999996E   5   −6.4346500580877163E   3
                                                   8.4479759022741198E   4
                                                  −5.7653848041538563E   5
I = 3   −7.4115800054554909E   0   2.2708602111336548E   6
           9.2339704254302219E   2   −5.43C0663552956542E   6
          −2.4951847165799923E   4   7.99C0452708907012E   6
           2.6020688357447893E   5   −7.0592082011546848E   6
          −1.41C0020778751853E   6   3.4320878162051124E   6
           4.5063438282596490E   6   −7.0543199999999996E   5
          −8.9781521209175582E   6
           1.1293527545564736E   7
          −8.7271536476687065E   6
           3.7846962947980555E   6
          −7.0543199999999996E   5

COEFFICIENTS OF THE POLYNOMIALS $P^*_N(x)/(x - x_i)$ (continued)

(N = 11)

I = 8		
-1.3165723755829503E	0
1.7205419079390677E	2
-5.4215736977175454E	3
7.1935442730423631E	4
-4.9834180996460810E	5
2.0007610589184785E	6
-4.8936349314803510E	6
7.3837131971996869E	6
-6.6978207698503306E	6
3.3440664896906895E	6
-7.0543199999999996E	5

I = 9		
-1.1559677949621800E	0
1.5125148748028633E	2
-4.7842599947124444E	3
6.3896975326104365E	4
-4.4684284782901579E	5
1.8162255652787943E	6
-4.5099926736515003E	6
6.9264750230549018E	6
-6.4093269944862010E	6
3.2696237052019432E	6
-7.0543199999999996E	5

I = 10		
-1.0598482524262067E	0
1.3877669110040681E	2
-4.3996667724851778E	3
5.8991506942435271E	4
-4.1488660005838893E	5
1.6990738941449236E	6
-4.2591465766413207E	6
6.6163925077269460E	6
-6.2050273191705889E	6
3.2142788280601957E	6
-7.0543199999999996E	5

I = 11		
-1.0110054727555422E	0
1.3243059035450821E	2
-4.2033254270432571E	3
5.6471403690313621E	4
-3.9831451706792341E	5
1.6375270636813210E	6
-4.1250893009936673E	6
6.4470107363448353E	6
-6.0903164443090354E	6
3.1821231006133547E	6
-7.0543199999999996E	5

(N = 12)

I = 1		
-1.0846360047086505E	2
5.1559690463514868E	3
-9.2197417744400098E	4
8.5714252445951845E	5
-4.7460933446364146E	6
1.6790453363184529E	7
-3.9337864617272212F	7
6.1762577991757723E	7
-6.4272493552206260E	7
4.2529277095548145E	7
-1.6200004539231031E	7
2.7041559999999997E	6

I = 2		
-2.0858810712881092E	1
2.8188844868536833E	3
-6.6479439208806762E	4
7.0128491360441858E	5
-4.1637333025608902E	6
1.5376337170479366E	7
-3.7061910459840010E	7
5.9351358387366719E	7
-6.2655520668857880E	7
4.1907005475455303E	7
-1.6095295051758875E	7
2.7041559999999997E	6

I = 3		
-8.6919741157204271E	0
1.2803975480242917E	3
-4.1074814193766142E	4
5.1304538720347632E	5
-3.3712222550908341E	6
1.3295884596250262E	7
-3.3527129359225762E	7
5.5456243295603781E	7
-5.9965118501394067E	7
4.0847771543197928E	7
-1.5913826467919283E	7
2.7041559999999997E	6

I = 4		
-4.846360447860881E	0
7.3254291300181080E	2
-2.5556997895957546E	4
3.6126118341389741E	5
-2.6152764443786548E	6
1.1076903293286273E	7
-2.9447526345421914E	7
5.0691663294906863E	7
-5.6525292661719950E	7
3.9445899926225420E	7
-1.5666957684995938E	7
2.7041559999999997E	6

COEFFICIENTS OF THE POLYNOMIALS $P_N^*(x)/(x - x_i)$ (continued)

(N = 12)   (N = 12)

I = 5
-3.1637134669205124E 0
 4.8353021794307799E 2
-1.7471512020308725E 4
 2.6141286017492770E 5
-2.0231540762048545E 6
 9.1043508787125055E 6
-2.5464049880790633E 7
 4.5694292253791938E 7
-5.2710180022588897E 7
 3.7820359472091702E 7
-1.5370194877502458E 7
 2.7041559999999997E 6

I = 9
-1.2599870047140484E 0
 1.9497040599509899E 2
-7.3218217916731509E 3
 1.1689929917037160E 5
-9.8783069732488354E 5
 4.9304114429093684E 6
-1.5400474144556435E 7
 3.0878277145750017E 7
-3.9660450849491608E 7
 3.1504903076266019E 7
-1.4078758315004055E 7
 2.7041559999999997E 6

I = 6
-2.2863241685378454E 0
 3.5143929209710211E 2
-1.2928158809267999E 4
 1.9930308733532563E 5
-1.6040779780371227E 6
 7.5375947230744220E 6
-2.1984244415561091E 7
 4.0977906012483762E 7
-4.8875309586617880E 7
 3.6099436277086302E 7
-1.5042183336513365E 7
 2.7041559999999997E 6

I = 10
-1.1300056337172179E 0
 1.7500396674272806E 2
-6.5890583909215897E 3
 1.0566789120384421E 5
-8.9861676621078778E 5
 4.5225980977865116E 6
-1.4272579036542971E 7
 2.8967374689262465E 7
-3.7728374331019435E 7
 3.0438086864005065E 7
-1.3831889532080709E 7
 2.7041559999999997E 6

I = 7
-1.7774090109071494E 0
 2.7411662295578018E 2
-1.0187901165548796E 4
 1.5981057468493164E 5
-1.3172190226655804E 6
 6.3696597527710023E 6
-1.9166647853966715E 7
 3.6864614913043415E 7
-4.5307106764057242E 7
 3.4406182911952595E 7
-1.4703532663486626E 7
 2.7041559999999997E 6

I = 11
-1.0503554746915142E 0
 1.6275220867507407E 2
-6.1374873546002177E 3
 9.8694040328699016E 4
-8.4260142802384212E 5
 4.2626519542308627E 6
-1.3539590592588064E 7
 2.7695463941829530E 7
-3.6404991281090407E 7
 2.9682634957866528E 7
-1.3650420948241117E 7
 2.7041559999999997E 6

I = 8
-1.4621684035776354E 0
 2.2596033460204436E 2
-8.4513913733253538E 3
 1.3400569981580237E 5
-1.1213286150317231E 6
 5.5263640115562262E 6
-1.7000298643450439E 7
 3.3493887768086902E 7
-4.2200025738625699E 7
 3.2846990697067090E 7
-1.4375521122497531E 7
 2.7041559999999997E 6

I = 12
-1.0093054712370985E 0
 1.5643295678174577E 2
-5.9040000513957906E 3
 9.5072538604817679E 4
-8.1332606983435926E 5
 4.1256067157586713E 6
-1.3148756650783668E 7
 2.7007540306116805E 7
-3.5676536042330501E 7
 2.9257811703237796E 7
-1.3545711460768960E 7
 2.7041559999999997E 6

COEFFICIENTS OF THE POLYNOMIALS $P_N^*(x)/(x - x_i)$ (continued)

N = 13   (N = 13)

I = 1	-1.2644666618088406E	2	I = 4	-5.5920489476150265E	0
	7.0245338566609323E	3		9.8648189703515587E	2
	-1.4736930837191650E	5		-4.0282425826881538E	4
	1.6173403145188693E	6		6.7036126249861326E	5
	-1.0667000989156791E	7		-5.7672967016894318E	6
	4.5522697896197054E	7		2.9412607766920006E	7
	-1.3097524020902081E	8		-9.5880735722672411E	7
	2.5909930830793518E	8		2.0770874136904664E	8
	-3.5307976886615008E	8		-3.0299336534799996E	8
	3.2566732552037564E	8		2.9448811625060757E	8
	-1.9416523890094218E	8		-1.8294253782839135E	8
	6.7521647139453050E	7		6.5744009269891590E	7
	-1.0400599999999997E	7		-1.0400599999999997E	7
I = 2	-2.4271373142518766E	1	I = 5	-3.6264255886560476E	0
	3.8282903577150858E	3		6.4685849459480753E	2
	-1.0586468226722062E	5		-2.7354641374455205E	4
	1.3178219165839184E	6		4.8160875083736626E	5
	-9.3172482038267787E	6		-4.4245701265234477E	6
	4.1498412167982543E	7		2.3943278663642275E	7
	-1.2281557116129343E	8		-8.2012460865595144E	7
	2.4778035238250518E	8		1.8499071129263068E	8
	-3.4250008457189322E	8		-2.7887545939564368E	8
	3.1929514242580019E	8		2.7843637866464456E	8
	-1.9193155229102627E	8		-1.7684807380864753E	8
	6.7175386955479225E	7		6.4735896853214817E	7
	-1.0400599999999997E	7		-1.0400599999999997E	7
I = 3	-1.0079532080862405E	1	I = 6	-2.5989495323157711E	0
	1.7328778717481911E	3		4.6625427624587220E	2
	-6.5084769641774461E	4		-2.0073625338023464E	4
	9.5831383449131965E	5		3.6407741793960885E	5
	-7.4929847037156251E	6		-3.4764135843287364E	6
	3.5621381825677600E	7		1.9623634618423213E	7
	-1.1024115446467419E	8		-7.0002386979225548E	7
	2.2964364791696371E	8		1.6379082336259820E	8
	-3.2504456994910872E	8		-2.5495904554972064E	8
	3.0854183556664098E	8		2.6170448342966822E	8
	-1.8809455571035112E	8		-1.7022701675121494E	8
	6.6572046545240404E	7		6.3602052380461468E	7
	-1.0400599999999997E	7		-1.0400599999999997E	7

COEFFICIENTS OF THE POLYNOMIALS $P_N^*(x)/(x - x_i)$ (continued)

(N = 13)   (N = 13)

I = 7
-1.9999999993815436E	0
3.6000000000123684E	2
-1.5659999999997520E	4
2.8900000000000462E	5
-2.8253999999999903E	6
1.6403232000000004E	7
-6.0310559999999959E	7
1.4542752000000000E	8
-2.3292821999999988E	8
2.4545415999999997E	8
-1.6349743199999997E	8
6.2403599999999994E	7
-1.0400599999999997E	7

I = 10
-1.2177676936436228E	0
2.2015076569271325E	2
-9.7054250796887763E	3
1.8321872369928457E	5
-1.8491574719641130E	6
1.1176499795303473E	7
-4.3087072104590822E	7
1.0952267673582392E	8
-1.8554999183803184E	8
2.0714875218926862E	8
-1.4619803585958379E	8
5.9063190730108381E	7
-1.0400599999999997E	7

I = 8
-1.6254106056596526E	0
2.9318277109505461E	2
-1.2835570496795085E	4
2.3946269059727593E	5
-2.3767360347638797E	6
1.4060256821494025E	7
-5.2823008723021107E	7
1.3036006216061560E	8
-2.1379280571123437E	8
2.3058480315709959E	8
-1.5704404056613858E	8
6.1205147619538493E	7
-1.0400599999999997E	7

I = 11
-1.1101378018099978E	0
2.0081267987063617E	2
-8.8690991095228780E	3
1.6795375306645290E	5
-1.7026697369629478E	6
1.0351309566871662E	7
-4.0194985295797689E	7
1.0305335658963001E	8
-1.7633237685047204E	8
1.9907316154864726E	8
-1.4224164371270643E	8
5.8235153454759565E	7
-1.0400599999999997E	7

I = 9
-1.3807455970296302E	0
2.4938924171174625E	2
-1.0963963406246212E	4
2.0600177182384753E	5
-2.0651787550968805E	6
1.2374017389442381E	7
-4.7200090695790395E	7
1.1850142742212464E	8
-1.9798539202253468E	8
2.1770203249501509E	8
-1.5119280842328439E	8
6.0071303146785144E	7
-1.0400599999999997E	7

I = 12
-1.0429712124155514E	0
1.8873297856413446E	2
-8.3450914692857729E	3
1.5833858496359860E	5
-1.6096815846965457E	6
9.8220090495688871E	6
-3.8315116413652576E	7
9.8778976478833246E	7
-1.7012180818179753E	8
1.9350609793310384E	8
-1.3944189578075447E	8
5.7631813044520736E	7
-1.0400599999999997E	7

COEFFICIENTS OF THE POLYNOMIALS $P_N^*(x)/(x - x_i)$ (continued)

(N = 13)

(N = 14)

I = 13

-1.0079714339254337E	0
1.8243480926385013E	2
-8.0713976179701241E	3
1.5330097898008718E	5
-1.5607421072744911E	6
9.5417344384770821E	6
-3.7311857364665285E	7
9.6475435981292942E	7
-1.6673481171541166E	8
1.9042647081912748E	8
-1.3786672036695841E	8
5.7285552860546910E	7
-1.04C0599999999997E	7

I = 3

-1.1574162157582346E	1
2.2966128234428255E	3
-9.9808481529112568E	4
1.7096370673251734E	6
-1.5664736490572809E	7
8.8131683554205348E	7
-3.2713902258233025E	8
8.3257505630568537E	8
-1.4779539988498051E	9
1.8294164821220530E	9
-1.5486318536737290E	9
8.5488782922267069E	8
-2.7735015213806377E	8
4.0116599999999991E	7

N = 14

I = 1

-1.4581307272487395E	2
9.3592930947540411E	3
-2.2757146947683914E	5
2.9087565319279455E	6
-2.2499462811690378E	7
1.1370404087734706E	8
-3.9256365898413462E	8
9.4914118241443450E	8
-1.6226264769256814E	9
1.9521312846090259E	9
-1.6164795526579096E	9
8.7692672246302460E	8
-2.8054107651998323E	8
4.0116599999999991E	7

I = 4

-6.3957614994002938E	0
1.3022041497202840E	3
-6.1513128408473107E	4
1.1896555879521171E	6
-1.1981847811414085E	7
7.2255528335757803E	7
-2.8231372004949396E	8
7.4676425157665553E	8
-1.3655274325948366E	9
1.7299700043088133E	9
-1.4917937922113523E	9
8.3592479863585360E	8
-2.7454382727258410E	8
4.0116599999999991E	7

I = 2

-2.7946576521974572E	1
5.0877699303161687E	3
-1.6299086393618311E	5
2.3622999969343892E	6
-1.9583843820272490E	7
1.0327411926099296E	8
-3.6671946922631607E	8
9.0416930565976869E	8
-1.5678030641774037E	9
1.9062727573007699E	9
-1.5914037904035313E	9
8.6885374294133068E	8
-2.7938072542698896E	8
4.0116599999999991E	7

I = 5

-4.1258264544875089E	0
8.4940111152578693E	2
-4.1549543307380067E	4
8.4979835908125042E	5
-9.1315334289765778E	6
5.8371048055375104E	7
-2.3940203698940502E	8
6.5877451818192813E	8
-1.2439151879965757E	9
1.6177332191812966E	9
-1.4254071787365227E	9
8.1314437068440019E	8
-2.71C9291172266267E	8
4.0116599999999991E	7

COEFFICIENTS OF THE POLYNOMIALS $P_N^*(x)/(x - x_i)$ (continued)

(N = 14)   (N = 14)

I = 6   −2.9373422404746634E 0   I = 9   −1.5161710444089635E 0
           6.0821389113351660E 2   3.1609714815279392E 2
          −3.0289244915874815E 4   −1.6077330637822071E 4
           6.3808107291383246E 5   3.5090667757180237E 5
          −7.1229930356286548E 6   −4.1120883805107579E 6
           4.7456473659044271E 7   2.9060704866360045E 7
          −2.0249980523924233E 8   −1.3241567161503011E 8
           5.7740263089002769E 8   4.0429806385895066E 8
          −1.1246104691522116E 9   −8.4294751415744144E 8
           1.5021683094537714E 9   1.2024250314431123E 9
          −1.3542585457758164E 9   −1.1534911543210262E 9
           7.8789815524134700E 8   7.1108793568535144E 8
          −2.6715875162966619E 8   −2.5435704837033365E 8
           4.0116599999999991E 7   4.0116599999999991E 7

I = 7   −2.2422905941923687E 0   I = 10   −1.3199153079819723E 0
           4.6585315789288496E 2   2.7544005608686518E 2
          −2.3441235145497771E 4   −1.4049918526238642E 4
           5.0244970703016864E 5   3.0816075444211994E 5
          −5.7416323780458284E 6   −3.6362339215551870E 6
           3.9324448510673741E 7   2.5927127214786480E 7
          −1.7281744290778779E 8   −1.1941162739159811E 8
           5.0733061810099195E 8   3.6912929785643342E 8
          −1.0156201690733840E 9   −7.8025480169954208E 8
           1.3911041045129530E 9   1.1295302404722763E 9
          −1.2828439390025391E 9   −1.1003963250961381E 9
           7.6159324053700743E 8   6.8912423001244709E 8
          −2.6292529857765644E 8   −2.5042288827733718E 8
           4.0116599999999991E 7   4.0116599999999991E 7

I = 8   −1.8049646329078541E 0   I = 11   −1.1853305552511130E 0
           3.7578467676169373E 2   2.4751442840690915E 2
          −1.9031935799825059E 4   −1.2650424287517785E 4
           4.1241287621471975E 5   2.7839810745686172E 5
          −4.7843243277375799E 6   −3.3007450983786692E 6
           3.3382697661047559E 7   2.3681141365139639E 7
          −1.4983658064213520E 8   −1.0989809578462970E 8
           4.4986285138408303E 8   3.4276783051801470E 8
          −9.2126560909521080E 8   −7.3194343166031732E 8
           1.2900962569385463E 9   1.0716230071987212E 9
          −1.2149596007792144E 9   −1.0568339927924811E 9
           7.3558445760512940E 8   6.7049367136484292E 8
          −2.5859050142234338E 8   −2.4697197272741568E 8
           4.0116599999999991E 7   4.0116599999999991E 7

COEFFICIENTS OF THE POLYNOMIALS $P_N^*(x)/(x - x_i)$ (continued)

(N = 14)

N = 15

I = 12

-1.0945698989293362E	0
2.2866164595891218E	2
-1.1702419723393073E	4
2.5811888195538307E	5
-3.0702047934302423E	6
2.2120224016802585E	7
-1.0319175583517772E	8
3.2386273118846253E	8
-6.9659163832994347E	8
1.0282640822576111E	9
-1.0233718266634360E	9
6.5578080356590451E	8
-2.4416564786193610E	8
4.0116599999999991E	7

I = 1

-1.6656281503583291E	2
1.2231904255938632E	4
-3.4113659259376478E	5
5.0207707923543667E	6
-4.4966831198449161E	7
2.6511483494478618E	8
-1.0787415823338886E	9
3.1162333115351086E	9
-6.4855027109461644E	9
9.7530538298919208E	9
-1.0498862328606564E	10
7.8860949321775678E	9
-3.9244775059985053E	9
1.1624501145869461E	9
-1.5511751999999998E	8

I = 13

-1.0371101427891460E	0
2.1671759998474038E	2
-1.1100486192908454E	4
2.4519315203212847E	5
-2.9224391985842803E	6
2.1112267750251985E	7
-9.8820046304836352E	7
3.1139543910837543E	8
-6.7295388233064583E	8
9.9880012110107125E	8
-1.0002071037698327E	9
6.4537983781746230E	8
-2.4213507457301090E	8
4.0116599999999991E	7

I = 2

-3.1884396056872881E	1
6.6356403417380977E	3
-2.4373579094520895E	5
4.0666700762636196E	6
-3.9028730249717708E	7
2.4008254354781750E	8
-1.0046383076688747E	9
2.9592651630077485E	9
-6.2463262239118417E	9
9.4929825630010373E	9
-1.0301966880242787E	10
7.7874933494715836E	9
-3.8950918981242009E	9
1.1585164020955917E	9
-1.5511751999999998E	8

I = 14

-1.0069047823547236E	0
2.1043628740523667E	2
-1.0783518111262497E	4
2.3837125475443361E	5
-2.8441945032002510E	6
2.0576174872217323E	7
-9.6481786447878885E	7
3.0468070295618936E	8
-6.6011574395699064E	8
9.8263765909997448E	8
-9.8735094411646730E	8
6.3952860422322554E	8
-2.4097472348001662E	8
4.0116599999999991E	7

I = 3

-1.3175801987560018E	1
2.9885907189998767E	3
-1.4877337284699804E	5
2.9317032602886405E	6
-3.1082200963825012E	7
2.0391280971058978E	8
-8.9171865038656949E	8
2.7106839576540919E	9
-5.8564678539087599E	9
9.0595452891132630E	9
-9.9680342913989256E	9
7.6179075692639344E	9
-3.8440235063014367E	9
1.1516084908331489E	9
-1.5511751999999998E	8

COEFFICIENTS OF THE POLYNOMIALS $P_N^*(x)/(x - x_i)$ (continued)

(N = 15)   (N = 15)

I = 4	-7.2573609683418567E	0	I = 7	-2.5037371186815562E	0
	1.6890973441824676E	3		5.9462820967314087E	2
	-9.1376725490805128E	4		-3.4264573377560644E	4
	2.0313590993403984E	6		8.4379803426580206E	5
	-2.3654503729479214E	7		-1.1133973678256492E	7
	1.6622265564157138E	8		8.8693731620030593E	7
	-7.6469843200354272E	8		-4.5792748152110425E	8
	2.4149028864505401E	9		1.6011978721570477E	9
	-5.3723899378805537E	9		-3.8907391799828809E	9
	8.5032145783714723E	9		6.6432116239475957E	9
	-9.5279838438689345E	9		-7.9440440592891955E	9
	7.3896231506956846E	9		6.5151354569540349E	9
	-3.7740682800167100E	9		-3.4915136019074064E	9
	1.1420075809663077E	9		1.1014270044497642E	9
	-1.5511751999999998E	8		-1.5511751999999998E	8

I = 5	-4.6617022772249185E	0	I = 8	-1.9999999901192495E	0
	1.0970770784434149E	3		4.7600000001976131E	2
	-6.1454861805632869E	4		-2.7607999999960472E	4
	1.4443125523029093E	6		6.8734400000007815E	5
	-1.7930899592615294E	7		-9.2067919999998402E	6
	1.3345340595477847E	8		7.4703440000000229E	7
	-6.4395782849385757E	8		-3.9377575999999939E	8
	2.1140484721628927E	9		1.4073497600000003E	9
	-4.8534013477272537E	9		-3.4956416599999986E	9
	7.8813357285103293E	9		6.0968317199999972E	9
	-9.0192310519957397E	9		-7.4385091199999995E	9
	7.1183137806629339E	9		6.2153985599999979E	9
	-3.6890032245624619E	9		-3.3885154799999996E	9
	1.1301065337020240E	9		1.0858226399999999E	9
	-1.5511751999999998E	8		-1.5511751999999998E	8

I = 6	-3.3011544877788310E	0	I = 9	-1.6650098393954805E	0
	7.8137945630630713E	2		3.9683010656080286E	2
	-4.4561031797562939E	4		-2.3115614641822985E	4
	1.0785497883883703E	6		5.7969713154270676E	5
	-1.3905090623848896E	7		-7.8439327865482412E	6
	1.0779398854364208E	8		6.4460155784839230E	7
	-5.4072029595592070E	8		-3.4487542895894915E	8
	1.8378528741743486E	9		1.2530451403345943E	9
	-4.3486692904945680E	9		-3.1670576123719569E	9
	7.2473157080254910E	9		5.6227381145203220E	9
	-8.4799085038268451E	9		-6.9819660060510262E	9
	6.8211751770212773E	9		5.9344986988532184E	9
	-3.5932443448646988E	9		-3.2886568640604687E	9
	1.1163925297316652E	9		1.0702182755502352E	9
	-1.5511751999999998E	8		-1.5511751999999998E	8

COEFFICIENTS OF THE POLYNOMIALS $P_N^*(x)/(x - x_i)$ (continued)

(N = 15)   (N = 15)

I = 10			I = 13	
-1.4345643795756188E	0	I = 13	-1.0821302913271892E	0
3.4223749970978118E	2		2.5854022148087629E	2
-1.9994618990982179E	4		-1.5173043862494899E	4
5.0394152936893976E	5		3.8535406088684495E	5
-6.8669710511203882E	6		-5.3082658433792913E	6
5.6940074737339605E	7		4.4638133558103793E	7
-3.0793105169336873E	8		-2.4559287741861397E	8
1.1326167563681392E	9		9.2182093736457115E	8
-2.9014838853350634E	9		-2.4167749132397433E	9
5.2255067461657444E	9		4.4662567959738925E	9
-6.5854823344066346E	9		-5.7892115871097735E	9
5.6819169222852101E	9		5.1476895013676626E	9
-3.1958357783530484E	9		-2.9888074454704959E	9
1.0552527502683342E	9		1.0200367891668504E	9
-1.5511751999999998E	8		-1.5511751999999998E	8

I = 11			I = 14	
-1.2730969010549415E	0	I = 14	-1.0323794228103793E	0
3.0392251022823426E	2		2.4670510782275951E	2
-1.7792902679574558E	4		-1.4487676284849932E	4
4.5002337213074037E	5		3.6834483466786886E	5
-6.1627019399477163E	6		-5.0817764644278797E	6
5.1427785627770297E	7		4.2819702885789743E	7
-2.8028954072007103E	8		-2.3617896989821569E	8
1.0403253648001468E	9		8.8915862209254824E	8
-2.6924031654720330E	9		-2.3393827394690709E	9
4.9035297017800658E	9		4.3408171474656098E	9
-6.2541611670470538E	9		-5.6525518329133008E	9
5.4641925653287248E	9		5.0521073445626454E	9
-3.1133126064361471E	9		-2.9500729088815034E	9
1.0415387462979754E	9		1.0131288779044076E	9
-1.5511751999999998E	8		-1.5511751999999998E	8

I = 12			I = 15	
-1.1598116800182083E	0	I = 15	-1.0060407163714017E	0
2.7700966416251313E	2		2.4043748365975074E	2
-1.6240833159135214E	4		-1.4124361524579518E	4
4.1177860837793618E	5		3.5931285982006877E	5
-5.6586769004905583E	6		-4.9612129778942301E	6
4.7436110584700149E	7		4.1848546858240318E	7
-2.5997785262680263E	8		-2.3113042032021602E	8
9.7131080496675607E	8		8.7155279693145856E	8
-2.5328663064844260E	9		-2.2974108527756640E	9
4.6522268248212248E	9		4.2722964284119848E	9
-5.9891050309552004E	9		-5.5772743622880040E	9
5.2853821741328186E	9		4.9989464172226760E	9
-3.0436640474547074E	9		-2.9282905809682015E	9
1.0296376990336918E	9		1.0091951654130533E	9
-1.5511751999999998E	8		-1.5511751999999998E	8

DERIVATIVES OF SHIFTED LEGENDRE POLYNOMIALS EVALUATED AT THE ROOTS, IN ORDER OF SMALLEST TO LARGEST ROOT

The derivative of the Legendre polynomial is given by the well known formula

$$(x^2 - 1)P_N'(x) = N[xP_N(x) - P_{N-1}(x)].$$

Since

$$P_N^*(x) = P_N(1 - 2x)$$

and

$$\frac{d}{dx} P_N^*(x) = -2P_N'(1 - 2x)$$

the derivative of the shifted polynomial is found from the equation

$$-2x(x - 1)\frac{d}{dx} P_N^*(x) = N[(1 - 2x)P_N^*(x) - P_{N-1}^*(x)].$$

When the derivatives are evaluated at the roots of $P_N^*(x)$, the following special equations determine $\left[\dfrac{d}{dx} P_N^*(x)\right]_{x=x_i}$:

$$\frac{d}{dx} P_N^*(x) = \frac{N}{2x(x - 1)} P_{N-1}^*(x)$$

$$P_0^*(x) = 1$$

$$P_1^*(x) = 1 - 2x$$

$$mP_m^*(x) = (2m - 1)(1 - 2x)P_{m-1}^*(x) - (m - 1)P_{m-2}^*(x),$$

$$m = 2, 3, \ldots, N - 1.$$

These tables give the values of the derivatives $P_N^{*\prime}(x_i)$ for $N = 3$, $4, \ldots, 15$ to seventeen significant figures, of which the first fifteen are believed to be correct.

Checks: Hand checks were made for low order polynomials and agreed with the machine computed results.

DERIVATIVES OF SHIFTED LEGENDRE POLYNOMIALS EVALUATED AT THE ROOTS,
IN ORDER OF SMALLEST TO LARGEST ROOT

For example, $P_3^{*'}(0.1127) = -6.0$

N = 3

```
-5.9999999999999946E   0
 3.0000000000000000E   0
-5.9999999999999910E   0
```

N = 4

```
-9.4332756589371306E   0
 3.7243057339114553E   0
-3.7243057339114553E   0
 9.4332756589371306E   0
```

N = 5

```
-1.3740666961489620E   1
 4.8517780726008331E   0
-3.7500000000000000E   0
 4.8517780726008319E   0
-1.3740666961489620E   1
```

N = 6

```
-1.8915986873541883E   1
 6.2770701859864077E   0
-4.2578674578469852E   0
 4.2578674578469852E   0
-6.2770701859864077E   0
 1.8915986873541883E   1
```

N = 7

```
-2.4956992249836211E   1
 7.9712213924980854E   0
-5.0083119828975966E   0
 4.3750000000000000E   0
-5.0083119828975966E   0
 7.9712213924980809E   0
-2.4956992249836155E   1
```

N = 8

```
-3.1862704825655723E   1
 9.9233405513433509E   0
-5.9356616715355759E   0
 4.7776387675098862E   0
-4.7776387675098854E   0
 5.9356616715355750E   0
-9.9233405513433438E   0
 3.1862704825655634E   1
```

N = 9

```
-3.9632641191050738E   1
 1.2128510598591098E   1
-7.0151138493662457E   0
 5.3499385187671730E   0
-4.9218750000000000E   0
 5.3499385187671712E   0
-7.0151138493662439E   0
 1.2128510598591092E   1
-3.9632641191050738E   1
```

N = 10

```
-4.8266539729459968E   1
 1.4584224552352508E   1
-8.2353816679842113E   0
 6.0482620784350391E   0
-5.2615698870016647E   0
 5.2615698870016647E   0
-6.0482620784350364E   0
 8.2353816679842113E   0
-1.4584224552352510E   1
 4.8266539729459968E   1
```

DERIVATIVES (continued)

N = 11

```
-5.7764248669798891E   1
 1.7289087349652058E   1
-9.5906545604471169E   0
 6.8527480037784513E   0
-5.7293788755183179E   0
 5.4140625000000000E   0
-5.7293788755183134E   0
 6.8527480037784522E   0
-9.5906545604471169E   0
 1.7289087349652040E   1
-5.7764248669798598E   1
```

N = 12

```
-6.8125674989402185E   1
 2.0242269444594649E   1
-1.1077665436970771E   1
 7.7531502769622777E   0
-6.2947105594040654E   0
 5.7114939261267680E   0
-5.7114939261267680E   0
 6.2947105594040654E   0
-7.7531502769622777E   0
 1.1077665436970771E   1
-2.0242269444594649E   1
 6.8125674989402185E   1
```

N = 13

```
-7.9350759068837505E   1
 2.3443251131591589E   1
-1.2694451159465853E   1
 8.7436888274613382E   0
-6.9417932937826653E   0
 6.1103956098434397E   0
-5.8652343750000000E   0
 6.1103956098434362E   0
-6.9417932937826653E   0
 8.7436888274613382E   0
-1.2694451159465853E   1
 2.3443251131591589E   1
-7.9350759068836936E   1
```

N = 14

```
-9.1439461254691583E   1
 2.6891692761957828E   1
-1.4439769180353670E   1
 9.8208762794436949E   0
-7.6617260993701775E   0
 6.5883903475806650E   0
-6.1321072119930342E   0
 6.1321072119930297E   0
-6.5883903475806650E   0
 7.6617260993701754E   0
-9.8208762794436914E   0
 1.4439769180353670E   1
-2.6891692761957828E   1
 9.1439461254690836E   1
```

N = 15

```
-1.0439175433552556E   2
 3.0587364457664123E   1
-1.6312799416456291E   1
 1.0982495249623600E   1
-8.4491321951165119E   0
 7.1328584764051239E   0
-6.4820514551937180E   0
 6.2841796875000000E   0
-6.4820514551937162E   0
 7.1328584764051230E   0
-8.4491321951165101E   0
 1.0982495249623593E   1
-1.6312799416456278E   1
 3.0587364457664123E   1
-1.0439175433552556E   2
```

THE ELEMENTS OF THE INVERSE
MATRIX WITH DIVISION BY WEIGHTS

In these tables, we present the inverses of the matrix $(w_i x_i^{j-1})$, $i_{ij} = i, 2 \ldots, N$, for various values of N.

THE ELEMENTS OF THE INVERSE MATRIX WITH DIVISION BY WEIGHTS

N = 3

ROW	1	5.3237900077244564E	0
		-1.6647580015448919E	1
		1.2000000000000015E	1
ROW	2	-1.5000000000000001E	0
		1.5000000000000001E	1
		-1.5000000000000001E	1
ROW	3	6.7620999227555164E	-1
		-7.3524199845511151E	0
		1.2000000000000022E	1

N = 4

ROW	1	8.7783059330622297E	0
		-4.9135573227363406E	1
		8.2366875462155330E	1
		-4.2664577893729180E	1
ROW	2	-2.4952495419778712E	0
		4.2343845761147278E	1
		-9.6261459981441781E	1
		5.7641919954205950E	1
ROW	3	1.2290561919335828E	0
		-2.2746685660881600E	1
		7.6664299881176080E	1
		-5.7641919954205950E	1
ROW	4	-6.5496972587503621E	-1
		1.2395555984240320E	1
		-4.5626858219032246E	1
		4.2664577893729180E	1

N = 5

ROW	1	1.3096091215873584E	1
		-1.1370836617381254E	2
		3.2621455387960418E	2
		-3.7977104240584473E	2
		1.5481333922979571E	2
ROW	2	-3.7321558320700493E	0
		9.5791727360612028E	1
		-3.6864824974282344E	2
		4.9250461742576776E	2
		-2.1703556145201710E	2
ROW	3	1.8750000000000001E	0
		-5.2500000000000000E	1
		2.8874999999999997E	2
		-4.7249999999999996E	2
		2.3624999999999998E	2
ROW	4	-1.1196222405308258E	0
		3.2133165655799880E	1
		-1.9334776617762277E	2
		3.7563762838230071E	2
		-2.1703556145201714E	2
ROW	5	6.4457574561629890E	-1
		-1.8660971287044596E	1
		1.1578146204084460E	2
		-2.3948231451333832E	2
		1.5481333922979571E	2

N = 6

ROW	1	1.8277283982094034E	1
		-2.2634124784500237E	2
		9.7307945300344727E	2
		-1.8868691372584120E	3
		1.6914494714837089E	3
		-5.7023452625728445E	2

INVERSE MATRIX WITH DIVISION BY WEIGHTS (continued)

(N = 6)

(N = 7)

ROW 2   −5.2137639562340929E 0   ROW 2   −6.9410653211762628E 0
            1.8819940606882597E   2   3.3499054543956470E   2
            −1.0787736580489966E 3   −2.6553296088702302E 3
            2.3907435979473152E   3   8.6058593537967719E   3
            −2.3099571975544721E 3   −1.3578219776863675E 4
            8.1606492177331446E   2   1.0377198349745988E   4
                                                     −3.0785879539985678E 3

ROW 3   2.6369381625442602E   0
            −1.0382467676719215E 2   ROW 3   3.5204555588708456E   0
            8.3478670215413366E   2   −1.8529521480577599E 2
            −2.2372330555568122E 3   2.0377373884617528E   3
            2.4295770882061886E   3   −7.9266328307875112E 3
            −9.2756392549416499E 2   1.3979217961099208E   4
                                                     −1.1496409792365218E 4
ROW 4   −1.6209292953026875E 0   3.5893498892626953E   3
            6.5461713775432119E   1
            −5.7508919022082158E 2
            1.7945639576737080E   3   ROW 4   −2.1874999999997508E 0
            −2.2082425392646358E 3   1.1812500000000047E   2
            9.2756392549416499E   2   −1.4174999999999977E 3
                                                     6.3524999999999991E   3
                                                     −1.2560624999999998E 4
ROW 5   1.0633062297524480E   0   1.1261249999999993E   4
            −4.3378702461460542E 1   −3.7537499999999992E 3
            3.9436316819925876E   2
            −1.3115640254625691E 3
            1.7703674113120992E   3   ROW 5   1.4878564240258433E   0
            −8.1606492177331446E 2   −8.1203287902127314E 1
                                                     1.0092970779827392E   3
                                                     −4.8131388752110666E 3
ROW 6   −6.3870289144857146E −1   1.0337417338213557E   4
            2.6164498964930826E   1   −1.0039689543210950E 4
            −2.4117639244238135E 2   3.5893498892626953E   3
            8.2341651389642276E   2
            −1.1597231598027144E 3   ROW 6   −1.0301560713205291E 0
            5.7023452625728445E   2   5.6505693626737353E   1
                                                     −7.1390602118058357E 2
                                                     3.5067953361693939E   3
                                                     −7.8710473381122500E 3
                         N = 7   8.0943293742454223E   3
                                                     −3.0785879539985696E 3

ROW 1   2.4321935531218214E   1   ROW 7   6.3505671861968320E −1
            −4.0620454164725030E 2   −3.4911537906430995E 1
            2.4240160528104807E   3   4.4427978535215783E   2
            −6.8911106957307754E 3   −2.2113580870537159E 3
            1.0105700100432974E   4   5.0658074548757152E   3
            −7.3801424274613136E 3   −5.3641853692384175E 3
            2.1240546327832863E   3   2.1240546327832911E   3

INVERSE MATRIX WITH DIVISION BY WEIGHTS (continued)

N = 8   (N = 8)

ROW 1   3.1230068535156645E   1   ROW 6   -1.4081395444206723E   0
             -6.7566361609514622E   2   9.9539951323624506E   1
              5.3201117676996218E   3   -1.6437571873641551E   3
             -2.0618588633533558E   4   1.0856214613981218E   4
              4.3667373451623321E   4   -3.4559345638578715E   4
             -5.15C7750348384053E   4   5.6179519216495687E   4
              3.1763023161459686E   4   -4.4749661063421699E   4
             -7.9803684875955420E   3   1.3823425769235606E   4

ROW 2   -8.9144666562789849E   0   ROW 7   1.0088738950588805E   0
              5.5415840227710723E   2   -7.1515869608280233E   1
             -5.7814946771425539E   3   1.1915715970485900E   3
              2.55C2564074450523E   4   -7.9955698673190570E   3
             -5.8041610578821786E   4   2.6057030694553029E   4
              7.1582884558008377E   4   -4.3705585221164779E   4
             -4.5470723191052204E   4   3.6178290078771015E   4
              1.1664144752831884E   4   -1.1664144752831895E   4
ROW 3   4.5275221271126113E   0
             -3.0689695082148951E   2   ROW 8   -6.3263629049736507E -1
              4.4110301906861959E   3   4.49C4361134187924E   1
             -2.3240704879435436E   4   -7.5130772461264898E   2
              5.8913236415820504E   4   5.0790321475309756E   3
             -7.7973493989913257E   4   -1.6738927934245614E   4
              5.2014319321227553E   4   2.8517349619132384E   4
             -1.3823425769235604E   4   -2.4099556251709168E   4
                                                         7.9803684875955651E   3

ROW 4   -2.8270116134000139E   0
              1.9662068346251237E   2
             -3.08C4548507999949E   3   N = 9
              1.8576680283564965E   4
             -5.2456397193370411E   4
              7.5267796535146267E   4   ROW 1   3.9001694289454228E   1
             -5.3354277602541823E   4   -1.0602788886162712E   3
              1.4854809783306004E   4   1.0622421003921418E   4
                                                        -5.35C8791074809902E   4
                                                         1.5253238835016151E   5
ROW 5   1.95C6271541061503E   0   -2.5700314282481323E   5
             -1.3714860269818447E   2   2.5355738385850332E   5
              2.2260096024338307E   3   -1.3536662111862863E   5
             -1.4261847226419701E   4   3.0188269946893946E   4
              4.3486763859943744E   4
             -6.7093136369321441E   4   ROW 2   -1.1134161372277153E   1
              5.0629390880600206E   4   8.6626630780324251E   2
             -1.4854809783306008E   4   -1.1479412061650056E   4
                                                         6.5739913426995402E   4
                                                        -2.0121824117593647E   5
                                                         3.5426794697368925E   5
                                                        -3.5986367476131020E   5
                                                         1.96C7904116239531E   5
                                                        -4.4381700059840438E   4

INVERSE MATRIX WITH DIVISION BY WEIGHTS (continued)

(N = 9)   (N = 9)

ROW	3	5.6589921408545195E	0	ROW	8	-9.9434922632873278E	-1
		-4.8003575926795249E	2			8.8408279628217183E	1
		8.7216161808651832E	3			-1.8725077842749459E	3
		-5.9461921498086391E	4			1.6335839433292153E	4
		2.0222663113608057E	5			-7.1786191232139593E	4
		-3.8138919379832646E	5			1.7262944053493600E	5
		4.0625635414618770E	5			-2.2999798830007584E	5
		-2.2906628353591240E	5			1.5897455931632836E	5
		5.3188530258027473E	4			-4.4381700059840465E	4

ROW	4	-3.5423371992372535E	0	ROW	9	6.3094690159005883E	-1
		3.0832612996598096E	2			-5.6144067147721140E	1
		-6.1012780666898347E	3			1.1922225317071455E	3
		4.7404503239454953E	4			-1.0448389121828567E	4
		-1.7882655111494329E	5			4.6224589234218766E	4
		3.6429059007332517E	5			-1.1218523386106615E	5
		-4.1108239647497182E	5			1.5126259454113333E	5
		2.4219992849559108E	5			-1.0613953845652293E	5
		-5.8191387545852712E	4			3.0188269946893946E	4

ROW	5	2.4609374999972026E	0
		-2.1656250000000560E	2
		4.4395312499999874E	3
		-3.6599062500000000E	4
		1.4850773437500001E	5
		-3.2376093750000003E	5
		3.8710546875000000E	5
		-2.3930156250000002E	5
		5.9825390624999998E	4

N = 10

ROW	6	-1.8076013195173521E	0	ROW	1	4.7636818940468489E	1
		1.5995412571005522E	2			-1.5888058270621540E	3
		-3.3374743057705762E	3			1.9703318379261181E	4
		2.8363935208562915E	4			-1.2468504388206205E	5
		-1.2000917873689352E	5			4.5693572875160750E	5
		2.7472299293684358E	5			-1.0264559981163606E	6
		-3.4504174828971008E	5			1.4345742062810324E	6
		2.2333117187123065E	5			-1.2163406599857453E	6
		-5.8191387545852729E	4			5.7263576347386928E	5
						-1.1482677561426949E	5

ROW	7	1.3561217085191610E	0	ROW	2	-1.3600251472079694E	1
		-1.2036985085192313E	2			1.2944478368158711E	3
		2.5359056832479502E	3			-2.1206736297286843E	4
		-2.1917518679328136E	4			1.5243922236262689E	5
		9.5003168642251800E	4			-5.9948947934919218E	5
		-2.2431467127417745E	5			1.4065755831522439E	6
		2.9207121661957015E	5			-2.0233284408266247E	6
		-1.9644195852830741E	5			1.7504102451139942E	6
		5.3188530258027473E	4			-8.3620979025510564E	5
						1.6952953248708086E	5

INVERSE MATRIX WITH DIVISION BY WEIGHTS (continued)

(N = 10)   (N = 10)

ROW 3   6.9152893859027954E   0   ROW 7   1.7134865755090915E   0
          -7.1754087313122738E   2   -1.8609271533055209E   2
           1.6062038367213613E   4   4.8294021180308756E   3
          -1.3712987612435867E   5   -5.2068450405179360E   4
           5.9817970742371711E   5   2.8754150696225994E   5
          -1.5014489889478536E   6   -8.9548791099261943E   5
           2.2625302986972632E   6   1.6320721886540262E   6
          -2.0238545415689603E   6   -1.7216549991630260E   6
           9.9117044050474624E   5   9.7183826091386488E   5
          -2.0479977286030388E   5   -2.2688995363410544E   5

ROW 4   -4.3347755028550114E   0   ROW 8   -1.3200922820458604E   0
           4.6152442191897273E   2   1.4363806009053172E   2
          -1.1245195102879295E   4   -3.7496162693666477E   3
           1.0907622419615872E   5   4.0840168876119671E   4
          -5.2619608282311886E   5   -2.2886025683627408E   5
           1.4230013082128769E   6   7.2643928184494508E   5
          -2.2667976051638034E   6   -1.3548600784180925E   6
           2.1149872426799043E   6   1.4672828405019311E   6
          -1.0701713217930839E   6   -8.5202751523798898E   5
           2.2688995363410535E   5   2.0479977286030388E   5

ROW 5   3.0224413129611460E   0   ROW 9   9.8397308027229257E -1
          -3.2536632332936194E   2   -1.0718187566739700E   2
           8.2120953859296896E   3   2.8074636043401075E   3
          -8.4433163665506096E   4   -3.0759373574475605E   4
           4.3694386813728240E   5   1.7385617851724621E   5
          -1.2605071027702074E   6   -5.5819292467264522E   5
           2.1208026082988289E   6   1.0561498767431684E   6
          -2.0701285705269394E   6   -1.1637950926080595E   6
           1.0870706834920285E   6   6.8955600212862186E   5
          -2.3764031359797455E   5   -1.6952953248708084E   5

ROW 6   -2.2391285740127440E   0   ROW 10   -6.2972078903648367E -1
           2.4240619103876510E   2   6.8631241594216109E   1
          -6.2282228225404789E   3   -1.8007322514163832E   3
           6.6004587961004892E   4   1.9787480981636393E   4
          -3.5578415857698541E   5   -1.1232455134290224E   5
           1.0751126718341503E   6   3.6273559299209234E   5
          -1.8939045898428090E   6   -6.9145818794948088E   5
           1.9286143921177947E   6   7.6901847430849219E   5
          -1.0516921388897424E   6   -4.6080521705455609E   5
           2.3764031359797455E   5   1.1482677561426949E   5

INVERSE MATRIX WITH DIVISION BY WEIGHTS (continued)

N = 11   (N = 11)

ROW   1   5.7135446067451098E   1   ROW   5   3.63684686962Ò1662E   0
              -2.2931949503718826E   3   -4.7010605445156681E   2
               3.4449271098965383E   4   1.4314916797832843E   4
              -2.6691108244372087E   5   -1.7923460126787861E   5
               1.2171732421675169E   6   1.1474710862920078E   6
              -3.4859840680927631E   6   -4.1974249472418496E   6
               6.4479931659584596E   6   9.3018408412827966E   6
              -7.6941942262124811E   6   -1.2725317995043416E   7
               5.7193040855846683E   6   1.0513146152103780E   7
              -2.4083425386946350E   6   -4.8113379976303542E   6
               4.3874883894089764E   5   9.3701110644666760E   5

ROW   2   -1.6312795060826556E   1   ROW   6   -2.7070312499433739E   0
               1.8644068765925653E   3   3.5191406250011327E   2
              -3.6965248445101517E   4   -1.0909335937499768E   4
               3.2513164279872124E   5   1.4076562500000030E   5
              -1.59C3665149134517E   6   -9.3785097656249920E   5
               4.7557994039214767E   6   3.5871304218749999E   6
              -9.0517670251565025E   6   -8.3037642187500004E   6
               1.1018601364003863E   7   1.1821497187499998E   7
              -8.3097665883900768E   6   -1.0116473554687500E   7
               3.5373012822365097E   6   4.7740661718749998E   6
              -6.4981738642925738E   5   -9.5481323437500007E   5

ROW   3   8.2966451112613759E   0   ROW   7   2.0925320056658747E   0
              -1.0336659056677011E   3   -2.7291771296296243E   2
               2.7931509968548526E   4   8.5470159711012349E   3
              -2.9127988457733486E   5   -1.1221276108008519E   5
               1.5783796218432105E   6   7.6580444244534033E   5
              -5.0444757345765935E   6   -3.0163378454905087E   6
               1.0050291820009005E   7   7.2126476877351874E   6
              -1.2642161324688680E   7   -1.0613016080694190E   7
               9.7693199820903249E   6   9.3766039635306394E   6
              -4.2366515626536198E   6   -4.5587730668363235E   6
               7.8967223585514622E   5   9.37C1110644666831E   5

ROW   4   -5.2049914834791204E   0   ROW   8   -1.6477565199383245E   0
               6.6541217343477771E   2   2.1533446996246072E   2
              -1.9562073819587268E   4   -6.7853720573353832E   3
               2.3125634510221724E   5   9.0030823198171674E   4
              -1.3828313593756115E   6   -6.2369982976702091E   5
               4.7527882042786382E   6   2.5040530553528363E   6
              -9.9945788459844315E   6   -6.1246301487788139E   6
               1.3096596717268065E   7   9.2410882893189505E   6
              -1.0445016032745879E   7   -8.3826594326138259E   6
               4.6435688045856577E   6   4.1852673378896447E   6
              -8.8288361424753016E   5   -8.8288361424753016E   5

INVERSE MATRIX WITH DIVISION BY WEIGHTS (continued)

(N = 11)   (N = 12)

ROW 9	1.2940094484292293E	0	ROW 2	-1.9271827278777505E	1
	-1.6931341404270634E	2		2.6044176581899662E	3
	5.3555796829983712E	3		-6.1421539686868955E	4
	-7.1527329877501948E	4		6.4792964058352175E	5
	5.0020326653882984E	5		-3.8469474672539422E	6
	-2.0331129052140852E	6		1.42C6472181404372E	7
	5.0485603123939783E	6		-3.4242160151656086E	7
	-7.7536105791211502E	6		5.4835778671494894E	7
	7.1747065316893241E	6		-5.7888553140109534E	7
	-3.6600707958978415E	6		3.8718629859132844E	7
	7.8967223585514622E	5		-1.4870730192057787E	7
				2.4984179627598569E	6

ROW 10	-9.7629228813438339E	-1			
	1.2783586044886945E	2	ROW 3	9.8031948403604127E	0
	-4.0528073056736406E	3		-1.4440892792927397E	3
	5.4340754123511167E	4		4.6326001574812138E	4
	-3.8217790816756704E	5		-5.7863539694710226E	5
	1.5651228711533300E	6		3.8022143389776340E	6
	-3.9233653943288432E	6		-1.4995689763531323E	7
	6.0947715541132936E	6		3.7813387059220001E	7
	-5.7158374375780773E	6		-6.2546016693490215E	7
	2.9608725820560665E	6		6.7631326608678409E	7
	-6.4981738642925809E	5		-4.6069932779512052E	7
				1.7948320996324875E	7
				-3.0498673596812062E	6

ROW 11	6.2880260228397588E	-1			
	-8.2366220639690865E	1			
	2.6142904642913728E	3	ROW 4	-6.1533573184439207E	0
	-3.5122822330838347E	4		9.3010244277611864E	2
	2.4773476663499336E	5		-3.2449465759824338E	4
	-1.0184725075194783E	6		4.5868972753631269E	5
	2.5656309060809547E	6		-3.32C5904613610197E	6
	-4.0097677383657286E	6		1.4064233819780233E	7
	3.7879189896733621E	6		-3.7389230994475974E	7
	-1.9791458507143508E	6		6.4362700153323064E	7
	4.3874883894089986E	5		-7.1769601275455609E	7
				5.0084066377137794E	7
				-1.9892180178185386E	7
	N = 12			3.4334399481678965E	6

ROW 1	6.7497577870255555E	1	ROW 5	4.3050516900768194E	0
	-3.2085918288893506E	3		-6.5796811365008522E	2
	5.7375030486017699E	4		2.3774517868851403E	4
	-5.3340516117344343E	5		-3.5571991182859019E	5
	2.9535236126994392E	6		2.7530251921105305E	6
	-1.0448804284925683E	7		-1.2388827732748150E	7
	2.4480199520641310E	7		3.4650435989768614E	7
	-3.8435239097435344E	7		-6.2178921116244563E	7
	3.9997175270065423E	7		7.1725853799073195E	7
	-2.6466235493385900E	7		-5.1464395928094344E	7
	1.0081364283854468E	7		2.0915131577516059E	7
	-1.6828132146723948E	6		-3.6797047140185474E	6

INVERSE MATRIX WITH DIVISION BY WEIGHTS (continued)

(N = 12)   (N = 12)

ROW 6			ROW 10		
−3.2133818890132765E	0		−1.2744705921293077E	0
4.9394074202290063E	2		1.9737725411676762E	2
−1.8170262969558237E	4		−7.4314329933278013E	3
2.8011641572128426E	5		1.1917694554195441E	5
−2.2544988126009934E	6		−1.0134999401397550E	6
1.0593935323414507E	7		5.1007872028815626E	6
−3.0898406193109324E	7		−1.6097249175721608E	7
5.7593609358735137E	7		3.2670693022309782E	7
−6.8693248668230175E	7		−4.2551737919709679E	7
5.0737019856009011E	7		3.4329427598729637E	7
−2.1141481234343713E	7		−1.5600219960168386E	7
3.8006359881257347E	6		3.0498673596812062E	6

ROW 7			ROW 11		
2.4981120366105657E	0		9.7044215838599398E	−1
−3.8526531093222118E	2		−1.5036966862586539E	2
1.4318886859061716E	4		5.6705340420244460E	3
−2.2461049637321472E	5		−9.1185184277300343E	4
1.8513244138972064E	6		7.7849448893550307E	5
−8.9524265939160105E	6		−3.9383401739558654E	6
2.6938331814258793E	7		1.2509469255818228E	7
−5.1812462789465349E	7		−2.5588333143219118E	7
6.3678212531130213E	7		3.3635220804861951E	7
−4.8357186859487314E	7		−2.7424315890347088E	7
2.0665514635039370E	7		1.2611867398300635E	7
−3.8006359881257347E	6		−2.4984179627598569E	6

ROW 8			ROW 12		
−1.9896588685466369E	0		−6.2809711593522656E	−1
3.0747756727657389E	2		9.7349208730042739E	1
−1.1500307185103597E	4		−3.6740962081756158E	3
1.8234946701209633E	5		5.9164236204064639E	4
−1.5258580461689787E	6		−5.0613790704191012E	5
7.5200497695790832E	6		2.5673908974999490E	6
−2.3133310008012746E	7		−8.1825536131977258E	6
4.5577110459247735E	7		1.6806961478158321E	7
−5.7424066378613165E	7		−2.2201731817901695E	7
4.4696839423953784E	7		1.8207319461822919E	7
−1.9561620276687946E	7		−8.4295810775418739E	6
3.6797047140185474E	6		1.6828132146723948E	6

ROW 9	
1.5997929543109294E	0
−2.4755198318961135E	2
9.2964442261825279E	3
−1.4842587620107125E	5
1.2542388006541802E	6
−6.2600943174096275E	6
1.9553828680241396E	7
−3.9205841039798698E	7
5.0356479548145109E	7
−4.0001461744518218E	7
1.7875659251661468E	7
−3.4334399481678965E	6

INVERSE MATRIX WITH DIVISION BY WEIGHTS (continued)

N = 13   (N = 13)

ROW 1	7.8723215761741140E	1	ROW 4	-7.1800957850138908E	0
	-4.3733370845262715E	3		1.2666259857964048E	3
	9.1749242665085137E	4		-5.1721949968460538E	4
	-1.0069243767794926E	6		8.6073246503961797E	5
	6.6410657217236046E	6		-7.4051109220683404E	6
	-2.8341539376074553E	7		3.7765288364222628E	7
	8.1542617182732684E	7		-1.2310923471440700E	8
	-1.6131015049827439E	8		2.6669449291041908E	8
	2.1982054304060176E	8		-3.8903833027967230E	8
	-2.0275409315113725E	8		3.7811773502616929E	8
	1.2088347172050379E	8		-2.3489510858476933E	8
	-4.2037653952405289E	7		8.4414190267413199E	7
	6.4752096878560858E	6		-1.3354193591861322E	7

ROW 2	-2.2477370421262290E	1	ROW 5	5.0275686325452575E	0
	3.5453247719127136E	3		-8.9678538759857406E	2
	-9.8039763299630777E	4		3.7923661623980344E	4
	1.2204159688198267E	6		-6.6768805526948300E	5
	-8.6285698775476013E	6		6.1340924932227860E	6
	3.8431084088931091E	7		-3.3194249772054336E	7
	-1.1373773829282458E	8		1.1369963774122786E	8
	2.2946582918524151E	8		-2.5646562287570424E	8
	-3.1718441412570172E	8		3.8662464671274063E	8
	2.9569465014906146E	8		-3.8601591823993492E	8
	-1.7774505673994069E	8		2.4517691232592228E	8
	6.2210162026014028E	7		-8.9747922978760178E	7
	-9.6318464320358678E	6		1.4419082659029207E	7

ROW 3	1.1435022541386730E	1	ROW 6	-3.7592935456641462E	0
	-1.9659144259815101E	3		6.7442121116049928E	2
	7.3837337089062175E	4		-2.9035827449897250E	4
	-1.0871874022740741E	6		5.2662580414283545E	5
	8.5006375595486111E	6		-5.0285159396617000E	6
	-4.0411727534986496E	7		2.8384930929296213E	7
	1.2506633008148411E	8		-1.0125611070161890E	8
	-2.6052601146065098E	8		2.3691794605853075E	8
	3.6875640203383301E	8		-3.6878972924484733E	8
	-3.5003438814031796E	8		3.7854677945665730E	8
	2.1338941800123314E	8		-2.4622768445999709E	8
	-7.5524622250712436E	7		9.1998240839950007E	7
	1.1799267514585960E	7		-1.5044119928021750E	7

INVERSE MATRIX WITH DIVISION BY WEIGHTS (continued)

(N = 13)   (N = 13)

ROW 7	2.9326171865931524E	0	ROW 10	-1.5635930168289730E	0
	-5.2787109375181370E	2		2.8266984063005935E	2
	2.2962392578121368E	4		-1.2461600812017583E	4
	-4.2376318359375679E	5		2.3524972654789122E	5
	4.1429083007812357E	6		-2.3742867586913878E	6
	-2.4052200046875013E	7		1.4350435738888247E	7
	8.8433892421874986E	7		-5.5323068110608408E	7
	-2.1324162234375005E	8		1.4062525506500000E	8
	3.4154465071289043E	8		-2.3824303520694640E	8
	-3.5991154417968753E	8		2.6597547632328919E	8
	2.3973768959765626E	8		-1.8771579270607138E	8
	-9.1502934960937452E	7		7.5836132834922675E	7
	1.5250489160156250E	7		-1.3354193591861322E	7

ROW 8	-2.3511020598640754E	0	ROW 11	1.2594285811982555E	0
	4.2407906939828032E	2		-2.2781786917240802E	2
	-1.8566223285037696E	4		1.0061811146148933E	4
	3.4637477026634895E	5		-1.9054009023612005E	5
	-3.4378691560331815E	6		1.9316439162563247E	6
	2.0337691079489856E	7		-1.1743348528528327E	7
	-7.6406714822997638E	7		4.5600386924789528E	7
	1.8856146846996064E	8		-1.1691192072352216E	8
	-3.0924414061381724E	8		2.0004546717896123E	8
	3.3353320311084915E	8		-2.2584442129174058E	8
	-2.2715895046998282E	8		1.6137022920606962E	8
	8.8531198296311073E	7		-6.6066587924319071E	7
	-1.5044119928021759E	7		1.1799267514585960E	7

ROW 9	1.9142246499875847E	0	ROW 12	-9.6588067525150983E	-1
	-3.4574583105919689E	2		1.7478290350464979E	2
	1.5200112938218521E	4		-7.7282694742085222E	3
	-2.8559473259567055E	5		1.4663509169040684E	5
	2.8631024340338975E	6		-1.4907030198520536E	6
	-1.7154969863530420E	7		9.0960216544732137E	6
	6.5436802612952841E	7		-3.5483079564821120E	7
	-1.6428685625950096E	8		9.1477792834817694E	7
	2.7448106194385215E	8		-1.5754736564691813E	8
	-3.0181562617390200E	8		1.7920322086746436E	8
	2.0960921505548761E	8		-1.2913513896815356E	8
	-8.3281068929590240E	7		5.3371995158416360E	7
	1.4419082659029207E	7		-9.6318464320358678E	6

INVERSE MATRIX WITH DIVISION BY WEIGHTS (continued)

(N = 13)   (N = 14)

ROW 13   6.2754325654637299E -1   ROW 3   1.3192182617820492E   1
             -1.1358033616786227E   2   -2.6176698889118296E   3
              5.0250939417359639E   3   1.1376129841734059E   5
             -9.5442184513363592E   4   -1.9486373264239693E   6
              9.7168744238493758E   5   1.7854602486996702E   7
             -5.94C4968247002391E   6   -1.0045213191534392E   8
              2.3229631009709712E   7   3.7287171793201094E   8
             -6.0063715334328042E   7   -9.4896563883299247E   8
              1.0380582544492640E   8   1.6845659139820948E   9
             -1.1855578799994879E   8   -2.0851614127761668E   9
              8.5833117642547679E   7   1.7651242434039948E   9
             -3.5664862301867960E   7   -9.7439764600752436E   8
              6.4752096878561324E   6   3.1612256734183405E   8
                                                       -4.5724736356778663E   7

                      N = 14   ROW 4   -8.2853474326476312E   0
                                                       1.6869318547415678E   3
                                                      -7.9686780156054197E   4
ROW 1   9.0812360683122648E   1   1.5411315559997361E   6
             -5.8289663908500415E   3   -1.5521806435712599E   7
              1.4173147839983437E   5   9.3602951931119271E   7
             -1.8115731489675179E   6   -3.6572146347742995E   8
              1.4012662197215885E   7   9.6739086896436372E   8
             -7.0814860275012341E   7   -1.7689635876698026E   9
              2.4448859025156668E   8   2.2410783352539684E   9
             -5.9112499164775832E   8   -1.9325345179767811E   9
              1.01C5715360281456E   9   1.0828933169120638E   9
             -1.2157870827756104E   9   -3.5565600666245118E   8
              1.0067432324798758E   9   5.1968787273840320E   7
             -5.4614983639526490E   8
              1.7472094203401437E   8   ROW 5   5.8047100120011414E   0
             -2.4984612699675259E   7   -1.1950398764145499E   3
                                                       5.8456906195872146E   4
                                                      -1.1955987721625604E   6
ROW 2   -2.5929439201463448E   1   1.2847342006460523E   7
              4.7205431754918211E   3   -8.2123426856577079E   7
             -1.5122645500081639E   5   3.3681964482398094E   8
              2.1917930943190024E   6   -9.2684340544247767E   8
             -1.8170314609713513E   7   1.7500898366654424E   9
              9.5819965438593150E   7   -2.2760221055625930E   9
             -3.4025026907391877E   8   2.0054346475457756E   9
              8.3890787197135754E   8   -1.1440295227590735E   9
             -1.4546416517418852E   9   3.8140618763727154E   8
              1.7686811664738394E   9   -5.6440868814093239E   7
             -1.4765389168795163E   9
              8.0614132771670892E   8
             -2.5921549025240051E   8
              3.7221050666134787E   7

INVERSE MATRIX WITH DIVISION BY WEIGHTS (continued)

(N = 14)   (N = 14)

ROW	6	-4.3454135988984638E	0		ROW	9	2.2429767235996775E	0
		8.9977288895809568E	2				-4.6762438071711000E	2
		-4.4808975591669354E	4				2.3784307536560466E	4
		9.4395747735252921E	5				-5.1912052591405939E	5
		-1.0537536408041449E	7				6.0832968396819460E	6
		7.0205644801013580E	7				-4.2991511298815900E	7
		-2.9957197201463945E	8				1.9589166431292070E	8
		8.5419165997620484E	8				-5.9810609757789245E	8
		-1.6637140741651876E	9				1.2470305777461878E	9
		2.2222615089891282E	9				-1.7788305398299336E	9
		-2.0034483623153584E	9				1.7064392698706062E	9
		1.1655922524640842E	9				-1.0519615804934038E	9
		-3.9522642489514229E	8				3.7628797956669561E	8
		5.9347261881679837E	7				-5.9347261881679837E	7

ROW	7	3.3973558695126164E	0		ROW	10	-1.8570159670441667E	0
		-7.0582687382160127E	2				3.8752227436386075E	2
		3.5516457151650535E	4				-1.9767119057650299E	4
		-7.6127530737320325E	5				4.3355769719068177E	5
		8.6993044124878497E	6				-5.1158922177814720E	6
		-5.9581548577651694E	7				3.6477408002075732E	7
		2.6184043920873012E	8				-1.6800267212292606E	8
		-7.6867050936797527E	8				5.1933559363837709E	8
		1.5387939241834240E	9				-1.0977565123736863E	9
		-2.1076999149043911E	9				1.5891593037307991E	9
		1.9436719741531675E	9				-1.5481701995747760E	9
		-1.1539107699158282E	9				9.6954303861108765E	8
		3.9836531833996766E	8				-3.5232510694594063E	8
		-6.0781758986943001E	7				5.6440868814093256E	7

ROW	8	-2.7347513323003781E	0		ROW	11	1.5355287206549947E	0
		5.6936165213192459E	2				-3.2064094856206270E	2
		-2.8835806993612131E	4				1.6387909461964253E	4
		6.2485803994344184E	5				-3.6064900873616884E	5
		-7.2488607759359972E	6				4.2759286645132501E	6
		5.0579039189955796E	7				-3.0677579805035408E	7
		-2.2702150561159024E	8				1.4236676990651131E	8
		6.8159952264165770E	8				-4.4403634576475745E	8
		-1.3958347470868521E	9				9.4819133467042906E	8
		1.9546601596146256E	9				-1.3882270207062270E	9
		-1.8408185547487766E	9				1.3690686886524724E	9
		1.1145041508177713E	9				-8.6858664432219434E	8
		-3.9179754849029175E	8				3.1993822789747303E	8
		6.0781758986943046E	7				-5.1968787273840337E	7

INVERSE MATRIX WITH DIVISION BY WEIGHTS (continued)

(N = 14)   N = 15

ROW 12   -1.2475862872878002E 0   ROW 1   1.0376501328108695E 2
           2.6062760743378854E 2   -7.6202104731323245E 3
          -1.3338370065970572E 4   2.1252068208346212E 5
           2.9420284436159510E 5   -3.1278310698451214E 6
          -3.4994068475622545E 6   2.8013358416833149E 7
           2.5212540726810898E 7   -1.6516077951216618E 8
          -1.1761754061302749E 8   6.7203255776900618E 8
           3.6913741442142965E 8   -1.9413456172005867E 9
          -7.9397229603139809E 8   4.0403272170386737E 9
           1.1720111890432950E 9   -6.0759405391423797E 9
          -1.1664350161564190E 9   6.5405630226037913E 9
           7.4745627373425093E 8   -4.9128657269467712E 9
          -2.7829900529628854E 8   2.4448456450149438E 9
           4.5724736356778663E 7   -7.2418115383536223E 8
                                                    9.6634843253979356E 7

ROW 13   9.6225326102204800E -1
          -2.0107528477675455E 2   ROW 2   -2.9628043653751451E 1
           1.0299271598415000E 4   6.1660581986539462E 3
          -2.2749551893174259E 5   -2.2648742165996484E 5
           2.7115024074623436E 6   3.7788853936586152E 6
          -1.9588419447538741E 7   -3.6266797135706409E 7
           9.1687380045719235E 7   2.2309270240058793E 8
          -2.8891943525264185E 8   -9.3354340420157555E 8
           6.2438119257866002E 8   2.7498478339131064E 9
          -9.2670839285593817E 8   -5.8042945429333378E 9
           9.2801382186039873E 8   8.8211958375880542E 9
          -5.9879739664641621E 8   -9.5729310319347060E 9
           2.2465816840735164E 8   7.2363984094253614E 9
          -3.7221050666134787E 7   -3.6194492311270040E 9
                                                    1.0765320589309505E 9
                                                   -1.4414037028720833E 8

ROW 14   -6.2710015336752826E -1
           1.3105968947461725E 2   ROW 3   1.5074711637670372E 1
          -6.7159735259176835E 3   -3.4193093774843647E 3
           1.4845758311460084E 5   1.7021473889404092E 5
          -1.7713639267785440E 6   -3.3542232418031030E 6
           1.2814838745635070E 7   3.5561798593829068E 7
          -6.0088842697862014E 7   -2.3330092608530021E 8
           1.8975509790025219E 8   1.0202340266802601E 9
          -4.1111999022159260E 8   -3.1013504180675495E 9
           6.1198659250107416E 8   6.7005078094156992E 9
          -6.1492202573021756E 8   -1.0365215941370442E 10
           3.9829832256176550E 8   1.1404637279698206E 10
          -1.5007902306176511E 8   -8.7158079635307732E 9
           2.4984612699675454E 7   4.3980279865037519E 9
                                                   -1.3175794486888268E 9
                                                    1.7747321082681184E 8

INVERSE MATRIX WITH DIVISION BY WEIGHTS (continued)

(N = 15)   (N = 15)

ROW 4			ROW 7		
−9.46920477148'56481E	0		3.89310095757'90968E	0
2.2038877080535676E	3		−9.2459692960939818E	2
−1.1922583550614816E	5		5.3278534088860469E	4
2.65C4614225451339E	6		−1.3120350817554673E	6
−3.0863745176710732E	7		1.7312394046906264E	7
2.1688274440203389E	8		−1.3751130423589867E	8
−9.9775745931099350E	8		7.1203877735789555E	8
3.15C8987956921980E	9		−2.4897282238044153E	9
−7.0097464706489844E	9		6.0497726835068652E	9
1.1094760259234863E	10		−1.0329636183294681E	10
−1.2431850981447831E	10		1.2352321377315820E	10
9.6417768253899910E	9		−1.0130488499360412E	10
−4.9243003787383682E	9		5.4290104362649751E	9
1.4900600482643042E	9		−1.7126264949032889E	9
−2.0239306917933514E	8		2.4119471694668019E	8

ROW 5			ROW 8		
6.6366757804224806E	0		−3.1420898282268978E	0
−1.5618639807466130E	3		7.4781738284354597E	2
8.7490785271136708E	4		−4.3373408203062897E	4
−2.0562089908785519E	6		1.0798483007813729E	6
2.5527491884002974E	7		−1.4464283818359124E	7
−1.8999218192076637E	8		1.1736246005859413E	8
9.1677654852784140E	8		−6.1863940810546784E	8
−3.0096847588033313E	9		2.2110096937500007E	9
6.9095899441064218E	9		−5.4918100786376937E	9
−1.1220336871860512E	10		9.5783965132324179E	9
1.2840312126592392E	10		−1.1686231979296874E	10
−1.0134053583039219E	10		9.7646703451171861E	9
5.2518837322508158E	9		−5.3235100375488286E	9
−1.6088866717550688E	9		1.7058761446289060E	9
2.2083449926279574E	8		−2.4369659208984372E	8

ROW 6			ROW 9		
−4.9721421254779123E	0		2.5889504739788939E	0
1.1769003011118430E	3		−6.17C3749020648235E	2
−6.7117059857596003E	4		3.5942839536004922E	4
1.6244931453902897E	6		−9.0138035701734846E	5
−2.0943608396814630E	7		1.2196656755473451E	7
1.6235745200514672E	8		−1.0023012892975089E	8
−8.1442361197469743E	8		5.3625232965056888E	8
2.7681423968320388E	9		−1.9483799634265415E	9
−6.5498909091008945E	9		4.9245086201086980E	9
1.0915782300378533E	10		−8.7428855747374010E	9
−1.2772292374733804E	10		1.0856370799125858E	10
1.0273936760152022E	10		−9.2276471019543393E	9
−5.4120828456768790E	9		5.1135852446701193E	9
1.6814912316880212E	9		−1.6640995423502344E	9
−2.3363534134708312E	8		2.4119471694668024E	8

INVERSE MATRIX WITH DIVISION BY WEIGHTS (continued)

(N = 15)   (N = 15)

ROW 10   -2.1607162008941111E   0   ROW 13   1.2380879821621036E   0
             5.1547223722031541E   2   -2.9580129461898464E   2
            -3.0115551312727244E   4   1.7359797992470635E   4
             7.5902806615966635E   5   -4.4089167033317190E   5
            -1.0342913718250845E   7   6.0732983814260203E   6
             8.5762161473357529E   7   -5.1071425638269283E   7
            -4.6380045512426004E   8   2.8098796648938870E   8
             1.7059278828690426E   9   -1.0546746851127584E   9
            -4.3701651364934064E   9   2.7650829106753853E   9
             7.8705684074366296E   9   -5.1099381550101918E   9
            -9.9189402533916214E   9   6.6235585027413801E   9
             8.5580055666431062E   9   -5.8895796177452410E   9
            -4.8135128963171655E   9   3.4195573387888802E   9
             1.5894035471711422E   9   -1.1670455028865396E   9
            -2.3363534134708316E   8   1.7747321082681199E   8

ROW 11   1.8124562374223438E   0   ROW 14   -9.5932137311621863E -1
            -4.3268210683708749E   2   2.2924660988209599E   2
             2.5331031295984525E   4   -1.3462431737559214E   4
            -6.4067995698388457E   5   3.4227829881761366E   5
             8.7735879029926104E   6   -4.7221560872005645E   6
            -7.3215645062550382E   7   3.9789495277812445E   7
             3.9903681011349272E   8   -2.1946537164325632E   8
            -1.4810688760755450E   9   8.2623583095245365E   8
             3.8330647941030954E   9   -2.1738324227371337E   9
            -6.9809556413282462E   9   4.0336319906658939E   9
             8.9037946818235535E   9   -5.2525395858814758E   9
            -7.7791485387328335E   9   4.6945865520283236E   9
             4.4322964323493331E   9   -2.7413061611605975E   9
            -1.4827963179240717E   9   9.4143312508996554E   8
             2.2083449926279574E   8   -1.4414037028720833E   8

ROW 12   -1.5132903464993918E   0   ROW 15   6.2674149853395997E -1
             3.6143458277432464E   2   -1.4978732605988824E   2
            -2.1190591940271454E   4   8.7991702161708039E   3
             5.3727739053593719E   5   -2.2384410147771451E   5
            -7.3832858170017967E   6   3.0907278460126053E   6
             6.1893331012304866E   7   -2.6070735053350934E   7
            -3.3921194402664189E   8   1.4398922790198320E   8
             1.2673395948070376E   9   -5.4295844801437538E   8
            -3.3048142182153894E   9   1.4312370236964035E   9
             6.0700974692865230E   9   -2.6615478102933054E   9
            -7.8144193438137809E   9   3.4745206974952855E   9
             6.8962211361327158E   9   -3.1142349585227706E   9
            -3.9712890466219183E   9   1.8242613812673533E   9
             1.3434429202463890E   9   -6.2870665172034847E   8
            -2.0239306917933528E   8   9.6634843253979356E   7

NEGATIVES OF LOGARITHMS OF ROOTS OF SHIFTED LEGENDRE POLYNOMIALS

The negative logarithms tabulated are

$$t_i = -\ln x_i$$

where

$$P_N^*(x_i) = 0 \qquad \text{for } i = 1, 2, \ldots, N; \qquad N = 3, 4, \ldots, 15.$$

NEGATIVES OF LOGARITHMS OF ROOTS OF SHIFTED LEGENDRE POLYNOMIALS

For example, 2.183011 = -ln 0.1127 ...

N = 3	N = 8	N = 11	N = 14
2.183011	3.919296	4.520308	4.982325
0.693147	2.286055	2.874069	3.330295
0.119574	1.438709	2.003044	2.448775
	0.895796	1.425235	1.855635
	0.524726	1.007232	1.417266
	0.270804	0.693147	1.077505
N = 4	0.107214	0.454490	0.807498
	0.020055	0.275032	0.590541
2.667410		0.144938	0.416188
1.108634		0.058126	0.277568
0.400492		0.010945	0.170022
0.071960	N = 9		0.090362
			0.036438
	4.140187		0.006882
	2.501226	N = 12	
N = 5	1.643438		
	1.085084	4.686415	
3.059523	0.693147	3.037776	N = 15
1.466354	0.412298	2.162400	
0.693147	0.214821	1.578225	5.115372
0.262359	0.085541	1.151746	3.462117
0.048046	0.016048	0.826945	2.578382
		0.575157	1.982016
		0.379921	1.539381
		0.231101	1.194272
N = 6	N = 10	0.122223	0.917784
		0.049129	0.693147
3.388323	4.339217	0.009262	0.509831
1.775520	2.696097		0.360861
0.965769	1.830738		0.241453
0.479150	1.261241		0.148258
0.185601	0.854343	N = 13	0.078931
0.034348	0.554365		0.031866
	0.333101	4.839821	0.006022
	0.174705	3.189298	
	0.069852	2.310507	
N = 7	0.013133	1.721346	
		1.288247	
3.671195		0.955107	
2.046127		0.693147	
1.213762		0.485760	
0.693147		0.322624	
0.352509		0.197019	
0.138382		0.104484	
0.025775		0.042074	
		0.007940	

INDEX

Selected RAND Books

BELLMAN, RICHARD. *Adaptive Control Processes: A Guided Tour*. Princeton, N.J.: Princeton University Press, 1961.

BELLMAN, RICHARD. *Dynamic Programming*. Princeton, N.J.: Princeton University Press, 1957.

BELLMAN, RICHARD. *Introduction to Matrix Analysis*. New York: McGraw-Hill Book Company, Inc., 1960.

BELLMAN, RICHARD (ed.). *Mathematical Optimization Techniques*. Berkeley and Los Angeles: University of California Press, 1963.

BELLMAN, RICHARD, and KENNETH L. COOKE. *Differential-Difference Equations*. New York: Academic Press, 1963.

BELLMAN, RICHARD, and STUART E. DREYFUS. *Applied Dynamic Programming*. Princeton, N.J.: Princeton University Press, 1962.

BELLMAN, RICHARD E., HARRIET H. KAGIWADA, ROBERT E. KALABA, and MARCIA C. PRESTRUD. *Invariant Imbedding and Time-Dependent Transport Processes*, Modern Analytic and Computational Methods in Science and Mathematics, Vol. 2. New York: American Elsevier Publishing Company, Inc., 1964.

BELLMAN, RICHARD, and ROBERT E. KALABA. *Quasilinearization and Nonlinear Boundary-value Problems*, Modern Analytic and Computational Methods in Science and Mathematics, Vol. 3. New York: American Elsevier Publishing Company, Inc., 1965.

BELLMAN, RICHARD E., ROBERT E. KALABA, and MARCIA C. PRESTRUD. *Invariant Imbedding and Radiative Transfer in Slabs of Finite Thickness*, Modern Analytic and Computational Methods in Science and Mathematics, Vol. 1. New York: American Elsevier Publishing Company, Inc., 1963.

BUCHHEIM, ROBERT W., and the staff of The RAND Corporation. *New Space Handbook: Astronautics and Its Applications*. New York: Vintage Books, A Division of Random House, Inc., 1963.

DANTZIG, G. B. *Linear Programming and Extensions*. Princeton, N.J.: Princeton University Press, 1963.

DRESHER, MELVIN. *Games of Strategy: Theory and Applications*. Englewood Cliffs, N.J.: Prentice-Hall, Inc., 1961.

DREYFUS, STUART. *Dynamic Programming and the Calculus of Variations*. New York: Academic Press, 1965.

DUBYAGO, A. D. *The Determination of Orbits*. Translated by R. D. Burke, G. Gordon, L. N. Rowell, and F. T. Smith. New York: The Macmillan Company, 1961.

EDELEN, DOMINIC G. B. *The Structure of Field Space: An Axiomatic Formulation of Field Physics*. Berkely and Los Angeles: University of California Press, 1962.

FORD, L. R., JR., and D. R. FULKERSON. *Flows in Networks*. Princeton, N.J.: Princeton University Press, 1962.

HARRIS, THEODORE E. *The Theory of Branching Processes*. Berlin, Germany: Springer-Verlag, 1963; Englewood Cliffs, N.J.: Prentice-Hall, Inc., 1964.

HITCH, CHARLES J., and ROLAND McKEAN. *The Economics of Defense in the Nuclear Age*. Cambridge, Mass.: Harvard University Press, 1960.

JUDD, WILLIAM R. (Ed.). *State of Stress in the Earth's Crust*. New York: American Elsevier Publishing Company, Inc., 1964.

QUADE, EDWARD S. (ed.). *Analysis for Military Decisions*. Chicago: Rand McNally & Company. Amsterdam: North-Holland Publishing Company, 1964.

SELIN, IVAN. *Detection Theory*. Princeton, N.J.: Princeton University Press, 1965.

WILLIAMS, J. D. *The Compleat Strategyst: Being a Primer on the Theory of Games of Strategy*. New York: McGraw-Hill Book Company, Inc., 1954.